Curriculum Associates

STARS

S trategies

T o

A chieve

R eading

S uccess

ACKNOWLEDGMENTS

Product Development

Developers and Authors: Deborah Adcock, Mary Ellen Osowski

Contributing Writers: Christopher Forest, Patricia Delanie, Jeanine Farley, Jo Pitkin

Editorial Project Managers

Deborah Adcock, Dale Lyle

Design

Cover Designer: Matt Pollock

Book Designer: Pat Lucas

Illustration/Photography Credits

Shutterstock.com: Ryan Morgan/page 6, jo1/page 7, Monkey Business Images/page 18, Drimi/page 80, iofoto/page 128, Thomas Moens/page 135, james weston/page 136

Susan Hawk/pages 8, 26, 40, 57, 67, 74, 84, 86, 94, 96, 99, 110, 113, 115, 120, 129

©2010 JupiterImages Corporation: pages 11, 13, 16, 17, 21, 23, 28, 36, 42, 47, 50, 52, 60, 62, 68, 74, 76, 81, 89, 100, 102, 104, 108, 123, 134, 138, 140, 146

Courtesy of Wilma Mankiller/page 33

Jamie Ruh/pages 45, 60, 62, 68

Library of Congress, Prints and Photographs Division, LC-USZ62-43605/page 79

ISBN 978-0-7609-6369-2

©2010, 2006, 2000—Curriculum Associates, LLC
North Billerica, MA 01862

TABLE OF CONTENTS

PART ONE: Think About the Strategy

What Is Main Idea?

Everything you read has a main idea—newspaper and magazine articles, short stories, poems, and so on. A documentary, a movie, and a TV show also tell a story that has a main idea. The main idea tells what something is mostly about.

1 Write the name of a documentary or movie you watched recently.

_____

_____

2 Write three important things that happened in the documentary or movie.

_____

_____

_____

_____

_____

_____

_____

3 Write a sentence that tells what the documentary or movie was mostly about.

_____

_____

_____

Work with a Partner

- Take turns telling each other about articles, books, or short stories you have read.
- State your main ideas in one sentence.

How Do You Find the Main Idea?

You can find the main idea of most reading passages in the first or last sentence of the passage.

Read this passage about an act of rebellion. Think about the most important idea in the passage.

> Colonists in America were angry when the British put a tax on tea. On the night of December 16, 1773, several patriots boarded ships in Boston Harbor. The docked ships were filled with bales of tea, which the men threw overboard. This simple act of rebellion was one of many that led to the American Revolution.

1. Let's look at the chart below. The sentences in the small boxes on top tell about the main idea of the passage. But they do not tell the most important idea in the passage.

2. Look again at the passage. The first sentence in the passage does tell the most important idea.

3. Write this main idea in the empty box in the chart.

On the night of December 16, 1773, several patriots boarded ships in Boston Harbor.	The docked ships were filled with bales of tea, which the men threw overboard.	This simple act of rebellion was one of many that led to the American Revolution.

_____

_____

_____

_____

WHAT TO KNOW

The most important idea is called the **main idea**. The main idea identifies the topic and states the most important idea about it.

- The main idea answers the question "Which idea is most important to the topic?"
- The main idea is often found in the first or last sentence of a paragraph.
- The main idea is sometimes not found in any one sentence. You can figure out the main idea by thinking about all the ideas you have read about in the paragraph. Ask yourself, "What is the paragraph mostly about?"

Read this paragraph from a research report about beluga whales. As you read, think about the most important idea about belugas.

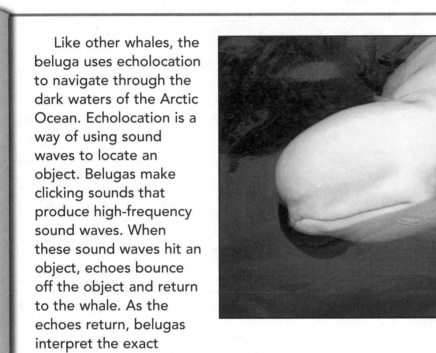

Like other whales, the beluga uses echolocation to navigate through the dark waters of the Arctic Ocean. Echolocation is a way of using sound waves to locate an object. Belugas make clicking sounds that produce high-frequency sound waves. When these sound waves hit an object, echoes bounce off the object and return to the whale. As the echoes return, belugas interpret the exact location of the object. With echolocation, beluga whales know where to find prey, or when to redirect the path of their travel.

The topic of the paragraph is beluga whales.

The most important idea about the beluga is in the first sentence, **Like other whales, the beluga uses echolocation to navigate through the dark waters of the Arctic Ocean.**

Read this paragraph about World Cup soccer. As you read, think about which idea is most important to the topic. Then answer the questions.

World Cup Soccer: Uniting the World

World Cup Soccer excites and unites the world. In 1921, the President of the World Football Association planned an international soccer contest. It was called the World Cup. Thirteen teams competed for the first World Cup in 1930. Uruguay won. From 1958 through 1998, World Cup games were played in Europe or the Americas. In 2002, the event was held in Asia for the first time. In all, teams from 75 nations have competed for the World Cup. Billions of people around the world watch these exciting matches. World Cup Soccer brings people together around the globe.

1. What is the main idea of the paragraph?
   - (A) Uruguay won the first World Cup in 1930.
   - (B) Billions of people watch World Cup games.
   - (C) World Cup Soccer excites and unites the world.
   - (D) The World Cup was held in Asia for the first time in 2002.

2. Where or how did you find the main idea?
   - (A) in the first sentence of the paragraph
   - (B) in the last sentence of the paragraph
   - (C) in the middle of the paragraph
   - (D) by thinking about which idea is most important in the paragraph

Work with a Partner

- Talk about your answers to the questions.
- Tell why you chose your answers.
- Then talk about what you have learned so far about finding main idea.

	REVIEW

The main idea identifies the topic and states the most important idea about it.

- As you read, think about what the paragraph is mostly about.
- Look at the first and the last sentences of the paragraph. The main idea of a paragraph is often found in one of those sentences.
- If the main idea is not in one sentence, think about all the ideas you have read about in the paragraph. Ask yourself, "What idea is most important in the paragraph?"

Read this story about a young woman traveling on her own. As you read, ask yourself, "What is the story mostly about?" Then answer the questions.

On Her Way

Miranda stepped on the bus, pausing for a moment to wave good-bye to her father. She was leaving for the summer—three months away from home and on her own for the first time. Her father smiled as he waved back to her, but his watery eyes told another story. Father would miss her greatly. They'd become so close since Mother died. But Miranda couldn't pass up the opportunity to travel to Mexico with other volunteers from her youth group. Together, they would work to rebuild a small village that had been destroyed by flooding. As Miranda took her seat on the bus, she felt the rumble of the bus's engine beneath her feet. It was time to go. Never had Miranda felt so excited, yet so nervous at the same time.

3. What is the story mostly about?
   - Ⓐ A young girl is excited and nervous about leaving home for the summer.
   - Ⓑ Youth-group volunteers travel to Mexico to help rebuild a village.
   - Ⓒ A father is going to miss his daughter while she is away from home for three months.
   - Ⓓ A small village in Mexico has been destroyed by flooding.

4. Where or how did you find the main idea?
   - Ⓐ in the first sentence of the paragraph
   - Ⓑ in the last sentence of the paragraph
   - Ⓒ in the middle of the paragraph
   - Ⓓ by thinking about which idea is most important in the paragraph

Which Answer Is Correct and Why?

Look at the answer choices for each question.
Read why each answer choice is correct or not correct.

3. **What is the story mostly about?**

   ⬤ **A young girl is excited and nervous about leaving home for the summer.**

   This answer is correct because it identifies the topic (Miranda is leaving home for the summer) and states the most important idea about it (She is both excited and nervous).

   Ⓑ **Youth-group volunteers travel to Mexico to help rebuild a village.**

   This answer is not correct because it tells about only one idea in the story. It does not state the most important idea about the topic.

   Ⓒ **A father is going to miss his daughter while she is away from home for three months.**

   This answer is not correct because it tells about only one idea in the story. The story is mostly about Miranda, not her father. This answer does not state the most important idea about the topic.

   Ⓓ **A small village in Mexico has been destroyed by flooding.**

   This answer is not correct because it tells about only one idea in the story. The story is mostly about Miranda's feelings on the day she is leaving home, not about the small village to which she is traveling.

4. **Where or how did you find the main idea?**

   Ⓐ **in the first sentence of the paragraph**

   This answer is not correct. The first sentence, *"Miranda stepped on the bus, pausing for a moment to wave good-bye to her father,"* does not state the main idea of the story.

   ⬤ **in the last sentence of the paragraph**

   This answer is correct because the last sentence, *"Never had Miranda felt so excited, yet so nervous at the same time,"* tells about the most important idea in the whole story.

   Ⓒ **in the middle of the paragraph**

   This answer is not correct because the middle of the paragraph tells about Miranda's father's feelings, not about Miranda, who the story is mostly about.

   Ⓓ **by thinking about which idea is most important in the paragraph**

   This answer is not correct because the main idea is in the last sentence of the paragraph.

MORE TO KNOW

- Each paragraph in a reading passage has one main idea. The entire reading passage also has one main idea. The main idea of an entire reading passage is often found in the first or last paragraph.
- The title of a reading passage often helps you identify the main idea.

Read this article about Cambodian dance. Then answer the questions.

An Ancient Art Almost Lost

Cambodian dance is an ancient art noted for its elegant and intricate movements. As the dancers perform, their careful movements act out a tale well-known to Cambodian audiences. The stories may be from a Cambodian folktale or an epic Hindu poem. Women usually dance both the male and female parts of the story. Traditionally, men dance only the part of the monkey, often a mischievous character.

Before communist rule began in 1975 in Cambodia, dancers played an important role at the royal palace at Phnom Penh. Just a few years after the Khmer Rouge regime took over, however, fewer than two dozen dancers remained. Most had been put to death by the new regime. Cambodian dance was almost lost along with them.

After the regime ended, many of the surviving dancers remained in Cambodia. Together, they formed the National Dance Company of Cambodia. They have performed on stages worldwide. Also, many dancers who had fled their ruined country passed on their tradition to young Cambodian immigrants. In the United States, the Cambodian-American Heritage Troupe is one of many small dance companies.

5. What is the main idea of the first paragraph?
   - Ⓐ Cambodian dance tells a familiar story.
   - Ⓑ Cambodian dancers are both men and women.
   - Ⓒ Cambodian dance is an ancient art known for elegant and intricate movements.
   - Ⓓ Most dance parts are performed by women.

6. What is paragraph 2 mostly about?
   - Ⓐ Cambodian dancers who performed at the royal palace
   - Ⓑ how Cambodian dance was almost lost
   - Ⓒ the important role dancers once played at the royal palace
   - Ⓓ dancers who formed a new dance company

7. Which of these best expresses the main idea of the article?
   - Ⓐ Cambodian dance is performed around the world.
   - Ⓑ Few forms of ancient dance exist today.
   - Ⓒ Cambodian dance recovered after being nearly destroyed.
   - Ⓓ Cambodian dance is noted for its elegant and intricate movements.

8. Which of these is also an appropriate title for the article?
   - Ⓐ "Cambodian Dance: Alive and Well"
   - Ⓑ "The Importance of Dance"
   - Ⓒ "Ancient Artists"
   - Ⓓ "The Study of Cambodian Dance"

Read this article about the Lost Colony. Then answer the questions.

The Lost Colony is the name given to an English colony that was established on Roanoke Island in 1587. The island is off the coast of what is now North Carolina. The colony is referred to as "lost" because no one knows what happened to the people who settled there.

The Lost Colony was England's second colony in America. Sir Walter Raleigh, an English explorer, began the first colony on Roanoke Island in 1585. The colony was meant to serve as a place to repair and supply English warships. Colonists soon discovered, however, that the seas around the island were too shallow for the ships. The land was also not productive for farming. The colonists in this first settlement quickly became discouraged and returned to England a year later. The English did not give up, however. Soon a new group of colonists was sent to the island.

A few days after the first colonists left, a group of ships with supplies and more colonists arrived at the island. But they didn't stay long. When the new colonists found that the others had left, most of them opted to sail back to England with the ships. Only about 15 people remained on the island.

Sir Walter Raleigh tried again to build a colony on Roanoke Island in 1587. When the ships dropped off the new colonists, they were promised that more ships would soon return with supplies. Once the ships were back in England, Sir Walter had them loaded with the promised supplies. Before he could send them back, however, war broke out between England and Spain. Sir Walter's ships were needed to help in the fight. By the time the ships were able to return to Roanoke, three years had passed. No traces of the colonists were found. The only clue left behind was the name of a nearby Native American group carved into a tree: CROATOAN.

9. Paragraph 2 mostly describes
   Ⓐ why the first colony failed.
   Ⓑ where the first colony was located.
   Ⓒ how the first colony survived.
   Ⓓ when colonists arrived in Roanoke.

10. The last paragraph mainly explains
   Ⓐ why the area was not suitable for ships seeking shelter.
   Ⓑ why supply ships could not return to Roanoke as soon as promised.
   Ⓒ what happened to members of the second colony.
   Ⓓ how Sir Walter Raleigh fought in a war for the English.

11. What is the article mostly about?
   Ⓐ the many colonies the English tried to establish in America
   Ⓑ the mysterious disappearance of English colonists in America
   Ⓒ colonists who struggled to survive in America
   Ⓓ a famous explorer who wanted to build colonies in America

12. The most appropriate title for the article is
   Ⓐ "Early Colonies in America."
   Ⓑ "One Island, Two Colonies."
   Ⓒ "The Mystery of the Lost Colony."
   Ⓓ "The People of Roanoke Island."

TEST TIPS

- A test question about the main idea may ask you what a paragraph or a reading passage is *mostly* or *mainly* about.
- A test question about the main idea may ask you to identify the main topic of a paragraph or of a reading passage.
- A test question about the main idea may ask you to choose an appropriate or a suitable title for a reading passage. A good title summarizes the main idea of the entire passage.

Read this article about an ancient Aztec myth. Then answer questions about the article. Choose the best answer for Numbers 13 and 14.

In the 1300s, the Aztec people built their capital city of Tenochtitlán, in Mexico. Near this magnificent city stood two towering volcanoes. They named one volcano Popocatépetl, meaning "smoking mountain." They named the other Ixtaccihuatl, meaning "white woman." These names trace back to an ancient Aztec myth.

According to one version of the myth, a great warrior named Popocatépetl fell in love with Ixtaccihuatl, a beautiful princess. She returned his love, and, for a time, they were quite happy together. While Popocatépetl was away fighting for the Aztec, his enemies tricked the princess into believing he had been killed in battle. The princess was so heartbroken that she died.

When Popocatépetl returned from war and learned of her death, he built a great pyramid—the volcano Ixtaccihuatl—for her burial place. He then lay down nearby, as the peak Popocatépetl, to guard her forever. Today, the 17,000-foot peak of Popocatépetl rises in the southeast of Mexico City, next to the smaller peak Ixtaccihuatl.

13. What is the main topic of the article?
- Ⓐ the origin of the names of two volcanoes in Mexico
- Ⓑ the love between a warrior and a princess
- Ⓒ the survival of an ancient culture
- Ⓓ a capital city created by the Aztec people

14. A good title for the article is
- Ⓐ "Betrayed by the Enemy."
- Ⓑ "Two Towering Volcanoes."
- Ⓒ "Smoking Mountain."
- Ⓓ "The Deadly Battle."

Read this article about Pancho Villa, a Mexican revolutionary. Then answer questions about the article. Choose the best answer for Numbers 15 and 16.

During the Mexican Revolution, Pancho Villa and others fought for control of the Mexican government. At first, the United States supported Villa's popular movement against the dictatorship. But Villa lost an important battle in 1915. The United States decided to support Venustiano Carranza, instead. Carranza was one of Villa's rivals.

Villa felt betrayed, and he killed several Americans in Mexico and New Mexico. President Woodrow Wilson reacted. He sent soldiers into Mexico to capture Villa. Villa was now considered a criminal by his former ally. Most Mexicans opposed this action. This included Carranza and his followers. They believed that the United States had no right to interfere in their revolution.

Wilson eventually withdrew the soldiers. He had not captured Villa. Relations between the United States and Mexico remained bitter throughout the revolution.

By 1920, Álvaro Obregón took control of the government from Carranza. After receiving a land grant from Obregón's government, Villa stopped fighting. Pancho Villa died in 1923, but his memory lives on.

Pancho Villa

15. Which of these best expresses the main idea of paragraph 2?
    Ⓐ The United States withdraws support for Pancho Villa.
    Ⓑ Pancho Villa becomes a national hero.
    Ⓒ Pancho Villa takes action after feeling betrayed by the United States.
    Ⓓ Relations between the United States and Mexico remain stable.

16. What is the best title for the article?
    Ⓐ "The Criminal, Pancho Villa"
    Ⓑ "Pancho Villa—Hero"
    Ⓒ "Revolutionary Goals"
    Ⓓ "Pancho Villa and the Mexican Revolution"

 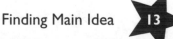

What Are Facts and Details?

Everything you read contains facts and details—stories, articles, reports, and so on. Drama shows and science programs that you watch on television also contain facts and details. The facts and details tell more about the main idea of these shows.

1 Write the main idea of a TV program or movie you watched recently.

_____

_____

_____

2 Write three important things that tell more about the main idea of the TV program or movie.

_____

_____

_____

_____

_____

_____

_____

Work with a Partner

- Tell your partner about a story or an article you have read.
- Take turns telling the main idea of the story or article.
- Then tell your partner three facts or details that support the main idea.

How Do You Find Facts and Details?

You can find the facts and details in a reading passage by thinking about the main idea. Once you know the main idea, you can find the details that support the main idea.

Read this passage about blue jays. Think about the main idea.

> Blue jays are not only unpopular with many birds, but also with many bird lovers. Most people who enjoy providing food for their feathered friends cringe at the sight of a hungry blue jay nearby. Blue jays are large and aggressive, and they often chase other birds away from the feeder. A group of blue jays can empty a filled bird feeder in just a few minutes.

1. First, let's find the main idea of the passage. It's in the first sentence.

2. Next, find the details that tell more about the main idea.

    Look at the chart below. The top box tells the main idea.

    The boxes below show two of the details that tell more about the main idea.

3. Add the missing detail to the empty box.

Blue jays are not only unpopular with many birds, but also with many bird lovers.		
Most people who enjoy providing food for their feathered friends cringe at the sight of a hungry blue jay nearby.	Blue jays are large and aggressive, and they often chase other birds away from the feeder.	_____ _____ _____ _____

WHAT TO KNOW

Sentences that help explain the main idea are **facts and details**. Facts and details support and tell more about the most important idea in a paragraph.

- Facts and details help you understand the main idea more completely.
- Facts and details explain the *who, what, when, where, why,* and *how* of the main idea.

Read this paragraph about facing challenges. The main idea is found in the first sentence and is underlined for you. As you read, think about the sentences that help explain the main idea.

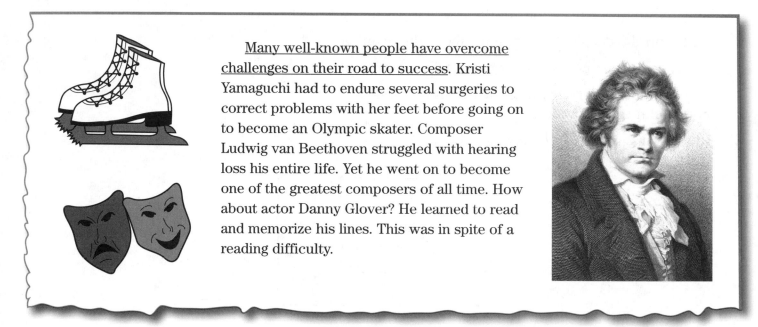

<u>Many well-known people have overcome challenges on their road to success.</u> Kristi Yamaguchi had to endure several surgeries to correct problems with her feet before going on to become an Olympic skater. Composer Ludwig van Beethoven struggled with hearing loss his entire life. Yet he went on to become one of the greatest composers of all time. How about actor Danny Glover? He learned to read and memorize his lines. This was in spite of a reading difficulty.

The sentences that help explain the main idea are:

Kristi Yamaguchi had to endure several surgeries to correct problems with her feet before going on to become an Olympic skater.

Composer Ludwig van Beethoven struggled with hearing loss his entire life. Yet he went on to become one of the greatest composers of all time.

How about actor Danny Glover?
He learned to read and memorize his lines. This was in spite of a reading difficulty.

Read this paragraph from an article about a marine ecologist. The main idea is found in the first sentence and is underlined for you. As you read, look for facts and details that help explain the main idea. Then answer the questions.

<u>After ten years, I still enjoy my work as a marine ecologist</u>. I am now studying how pollution affects the plants and animals of the ocean. I am interested in the effects of pollution on their growth and development. I also want to determine whether pollution affects the number and the variety of certain plants and animals. First, I will find whether the plants and animals are suffering or thriving. Then I will try to determine the effect of human behavior on them.

1. What is one thing that the marine ecologist studies?
   Ⓐ whether pollution affects the growth of land animals
   Ⓑ whether pollution affects the plants and animals of the ocean
   Ⓒ whether pollution affects human actions
   Ⓓ whether pollution affects the land

2. The first thing that the ecologist will do is
   Ⓐ find whether the plants and animals are suffering or thriving.
   Ⓑ determine the effect of human behavior on the plants and animals.
   Ⓒ decide whether to study plants or animals.
   Ⓓ discover how to prevent water pollution.

Work with a Partner

- Talk about your answers to the questions.
- Tell why you chose your answers.
- Then talk about what you have learned so far about recalling facts and details.

REVIEW

Facts and details explain or support the main idea.

- Look for sentences that provide information about the main idea.
- Look for sentences that explain the *who, what, where, when, why,* and *how* of the main idea.

Read this short article about laughter. As you read, ask yourself, "What is the main idea? Which sentences provide more information about the main idea?" Then answer the questions.

Laughter and Your Health

How much do you think you laugh each day? The average child laughs about 50 times a day, whereas the average adult laughs only 15 times. Laughter may not seem that important, but it may be more important than you realize.

Scientific studies have shown the healthful effects of laughter on body and mind. When you laugh, your body experiences the same benefits as it would from a workout. Your lungs fill with more oxygen, your heart pumps faster, and blood courses through your body. As a result, your heart rate and your blood pressure decrease to a more healthful level. Laughter also relieves stress by releasing hormones in the body. Your muscles relax, and your overall sense of well-being improves. Laughter may protect you from illness, too, by causing more antibodies that fight viruses to be produced.

3. How is laughter good for one's health?
   - Ⓐ Laughter brings oxygen to your lungs.
   - Ⓑ Laughing reduces blood pressure.
   - Ⓒ Laughter cures illness.
   - Ⓓ Laughing helps you sleep better at night.

4. Laughter may help protect people from illness because
   - Ⓐ most people laugh about 15 times a day.
   - Ⓑ it makes your heart pump faster.
   - Ⓒ it releases hormones in the body.
   - Ⓓ it produces antibodies that fight viruses.

Which Answer Is Correct and Why?

Look at the answer choices for each question.
Read why each answer choice is correct or not correct.

3. **How is laughter good for one's health?**

   Ⓐ **Laughter brings oxygen to your lungs.**

   This answer is not correct because, although laughing does bring oxygen to your lungs, this alone does not affect your health.

   ⬤ **Laughing reduces blood pressure.**

   This answer is correct because paragraph 2 explains that, when the lungs fill with more oxygen, your heart pumps faster, and blood courses through your body. As a result, your heart rate and your blood pressure decrease to a more healthful level.

   Ⓒ **Laughter cures illness.**

   This answer is not correct because laughing cannot cure an illness, but it may help protect against one.

   Ⓓ **Laughing helps you sleep better at night.**

   This answer is not correct because nothing is mentioned in the article about how laughter affects sleep.

4. **Laughter may help protect people from illness because**

   Ⓐ **most people laugh about 15 times a day.**

   This answer is not correct because most adults laugh about 15 times a day, whereas most children laugh about 50 times a day. Also, nothing is stated about the number of times a person laughs and how that relates to illness.

   Ⓑ **it makes your heart pump faster.**

   This answer is not correct because the heart's pumping faster does not affect how the body protects people from illness.

   Ⓒ **it releases hormones in the body.**

   This answer is not correct because the release of hormones does not affect how the body protects people from illness.

   ⬤ **it produces antibodies that fight viruses.**

   This answer is correct because laughing may help produce antibodies that help protect people from illness.

MORE TO KNOW	Facts and details give additional meaning to the main idea of a reading passage. When you read, look for sentences that

- describe a person, place, or thing.
- tell the order in which things happen.
- explain how to do something.

- share an experience, idea, or opinion.
- help you picture where a story takes place.
- understand what characters are like.

Read this report about Japanese warriors called samurai. Then answer the questions.

Tale of the Forty-seven Ronin

During the Edo period, a court official, Kira, insulted Lord Asano, who was visiting Edo Castle. Enraged, Lord Asano took out his sword and attacked Kira. The display of swords in the castle was illegal. Because Asano dishonored the shogun by breaking this law, Asano was ordered to commit *seppuku*. This ritual meant that he had to take his own life.

When Asano died, his band of *samurai* followers became *ronin*, or "masterless samurai." Forty-seven of these ronin swore to revenge their master's death by slaying Kira. They plotted their revenge for almost two years. Finally, they raided Kira's mansion and killed him. As a result, they too were ordered to commit seppuku.

The forty-seven ronin were buried at Sengakuji Temple in Edo (modern-day Tokyo), near the grave of Lord Asano. To this day, many tourists visit this site. The tale of the ronin is still told as a classic example of Japanese loyalty.

There are no longer any masterless samurai in Japan. The word *ronin* still exists, but it has a whole new meaning. Today, students who don't pass their university entrance exams on their first attempt are called ronin. The "masterless samurai" have become the "school-less students."

5. Who insulted Lord Asano?
   - Ⓐ the ronin
   - Ⓑ the samurai
   - Ⓒ the court official
   - Ⓓ the castle guard

6. Which detail would best fit in the passage?
   - Ⓐ During the early years of the Edo period, new forms of art were produced.
   - Ⓑ Japan is made up of four main islands.
   - Ⓒ The shogun had supreme rule and was to be respected.
   - Ⓓ U.S. Commodore Matthew Perry arrived in Japan in 1853.

7. The forty-seven ronin were buried
   - Ⓐ at Edo Castle.
   - Ⓑ at Sengakuji Temple.
   - Ⓒ near Kira's grave.
   - Ⓓ near Asano's home.

8. Which detail helps explain the main idea of the last paragraph?
   - Ⓐ The "masterless samurai" have become the "school-less students."
   - Ⓑ As a result, they too were ordered to commit seppuku.
   - Ⓒ They plotted their revenge for almost two years.
   - Ⓓ To this day, many tourists visit this site.

Read this selection from the journal of William Bradford, which was written in 1620, soon after the Pilgrims arrived near the coast of Plymouth, Massachusetts. Then answer the questions.

On this 10th day of November, before we harbored the ship, we observed some of our people were not interested in staying united and working in harmony with us. Instead they appeared dissatisfied. So it was thought there should be an agreement that we should join together in one body. We should by common consent agree to obey such government we made, and governors we chose.

We set our signatures to this document that follows word for word . . .

We whose names are signed below are loyal subjects of the mighty ruler, King James of Great Britain, France, and Ireland.

We have agreed, for the greater glory of God, the spreading of Christianity, and for the honor of our King and country, to build the first colony in northern Virginia.

We, by this document, solemnly do promise before God and one another, to join together into a group to form a citizen's government, so we may manage, keep safe, and improve this colony.

This government shall plan, make up, and make into law any fair and equal laws, rules, constitutions, and public positions that are necessary and useful for the good of the colony.

We all promise to obey.

9. What is one detail that explains why the Pilgrims formed an agreement?
   - Ⓐ Some of our people were not interested in staying united.
   - Ⓑ We set our signatures to this document.
   - Ⓒ We have agreed to build the first colony in northern Virginia.
   - Ⓓ We join together so we may manage, keep safe, and improve this colony.

10. Which of these is not a reason the Pilgrims agreed to build the new colony?
    - Ⓐ for the glory of God
    - Ⓑ to spread Christianity
    - Ⓒ for the honor of King and country
    - Ⓓ to advance themselves

11. The Pilgrims considered themselves to be loyal subjects of
    - Ⓐ the new governors.
    - Ⓑ Virginia.
    - Ⓒ King James.
    - Ⓓ William Bradford.

12. In their agreement, the Pilgrims promised to
    - Ⓐ form a citizen's government.
    - Ⓑ create a new religion.
    - Ⓒ return to England.
    - Ⓓ obey one another.

TEST TIPS

- A test question about facts and details may ask you to recall a specific fact or detail from a reading passage. Often, these test questions are *who, what, where, when, why,* and *how* questions.
- The answer to a test question about facts and details is always found in the reading passage. Review what you have read to help you find the answer.

Read this selection from the poem "The Highwayman." Then answer questions about the selection. Choose the best answer for Numbers 13 and 14.

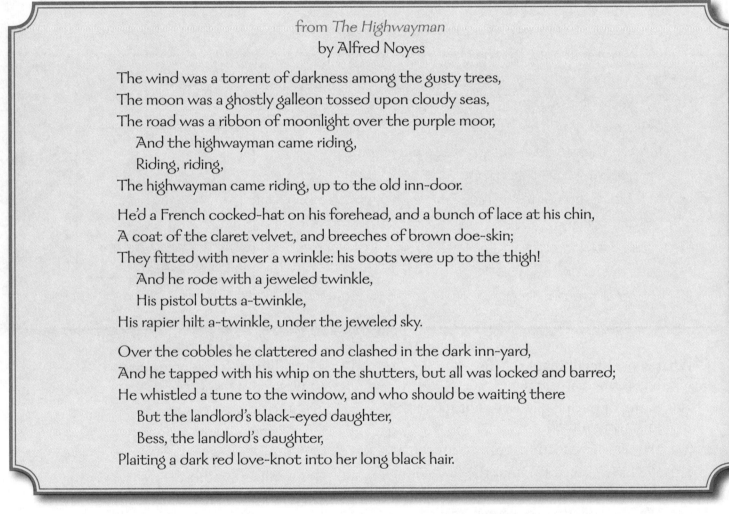

from *The Highwayman*
by Alfred Noyes

The wind was a torrent of darkness among the gusty trees,
The moon was a ghostly galleon tossed upon cloudy seas,
The road was a ribbon of moonlight over the purple moor,
    And the highwayman came riding,
    Riding, riding,
The highwayman came riding, up to the old inn-door.

He'd a French cocked-hat on his forehead, and a bunch of lace at his chin,
A coat of the claret velvet, and breeches of brown doe-skin;
They fitted with never a wrinkle: his boots were up to the thigh!
    And he rode with a jeweled twinkle,
    His pistol butts a-twinkle,
His rapier hilt a-twinkle, under the jeweled sky.

Over the cobbles he clattered and clashed in the dark inn-yard,
And he tapped with his whip on the shutters, but all was locked and barred;
He whistled a tune to the window, and who should be waiting there
    But the landlord's black-eyed daughter,
    Bess, the landlord's daughter,
Plaiting a dark red love-knot into her long black hair.

13. Which of these is <u>not</u> mentioned in the selection as something the highwayman was wearing?
  Ⓐ doe-skin breeches
  Ⓑ a velvet coat
  Ⓒ an English hat
  Ⓓ riding boots

14. The highwayman gets Bess's attention by
  Ⓐ tapping with his whip on the shutters.
  Ⓑ trotting over the cobblestones of the yard.
  Ⓒ rapping on the wooden door.
  Ⓓ whistling a tune to the window.

Read this article about Opo the Dolphin. Then answer questions about the article. Choose the best answer for Numbers 15 and 16.

The story of Opo the Dolphin took place in New Zealand. It was 1955 in Hokiango Harbor when a lone dolphin began to make itself known. At first people thought the dolphin was a shark, and they worried whenever it followed pleasure boats around the harbor. But then Opo's secret was discovered. Not only was the shark really a dolphin, but she was a youngster! Her purpose in following the boats had nothing to do with hunger. Like all children, Opo wanted only to play.

When summer arrived, Opo began to swim among the children at Opononi Beach. Opo quickly showed that she favored children over adults. One particular child, a thirteen-year-old girl named Jill Baker, became Opo's favorite. Whenever Opo saw Jill enter the water, she would leave the other children to swim to Jill. Opo would often dive under Jill, pick her up, and take her for a ride. Opo took many children for rides once she came to believe they were all her friends.

Many people came to Opononi Beach when the story of Opo the Dolphin became well-known. At times there were so many visitors, Opo was frightened away. Some of the tourists treated Opo roughly when they tried to pet her or swim with her. At such times Opo showed her displeasure by swimming away. She never gave any stronger sign of her anger, even when she was really injured.

There were a number of tricks Opo performed to entertain the children at the beach. She would throw a beach ball high into the air and then swim out quickly and catch it. She would jump through hoops that the children held above the water. After a trick, when she got her applause, she would leap high into the air as a way of taking her bow.

15. Opo favored mostly
- Ⓐ adults.
- Ⓑ children.
- Ⓒ girls.
- Ⓓ tourists.

16. Which of these would best fit in the article?
- Ⓐ Opo was afraid of sharks.
- Ⓑ Opo would safely return her riders to shallow water.
- Ⓒ Opo bit the tourists who treated her roughly.
- Ⓓ Opo disliked performing tricks.

What Is Sequence?

Most things you read are told in order. Directions for putting together a bookcase include a series of steps you must follow in order to successfully complete the task. A movie or history program usually tells about events in the order in which they happened. Many of the things you do each day are also done in a particular order.

 1 Write five things you did yesterday.

_____

_____

_____

_____

_____

2 Now list and number these things in the order in which you did them.

_____

_____

_____

_____

_____

 Work with a Partner

- Tell your partner about one of your favorite books or movies.
- Take turns telling about the beginning, the middle, and the ending of the movie. Try to use only one or two sentences to describe each part.

How Do You Find Sequence?

You can find sequence in many reading passages by thinking about the time order in which events are presented or by thinking about what happens first, second, third, and so on.

Read this passage about how colonists made thread from flax.
Pay attention to the order of the steps.

> Many colonists used flax to weave cloth that could be used to make clothing. First, the flax was harvested and allowed to dry. Next, it was bundled into stalks and soaked in a stream for several days. The flax was then dried again, the stalks were pounded and crushed, and the fibers were removed. The fibers were used to spin into a linen thread on a spinning wheel.

1. Let's find the order of the steps by which flax was prepared before it was spun.

2. Look at the chart below.

   The chart shows some of the steps that must be followed in order before flax can be spun into thread.

3. Fill in the missing information for the second step.

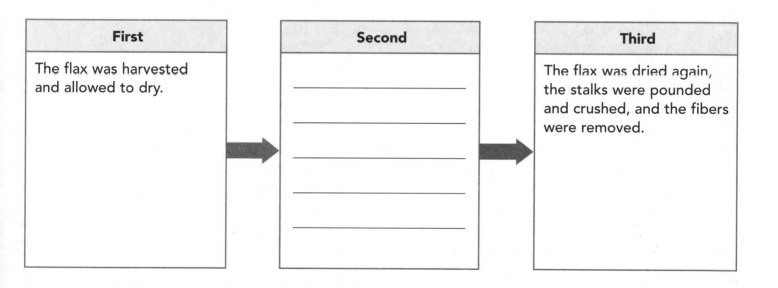

First	Second	Third
The flax was harvested and allowed to dry.	_____ _____ _____ _____ _____	The flax was dried again, the stalks were pounded and crushed, and the fibers were removed.

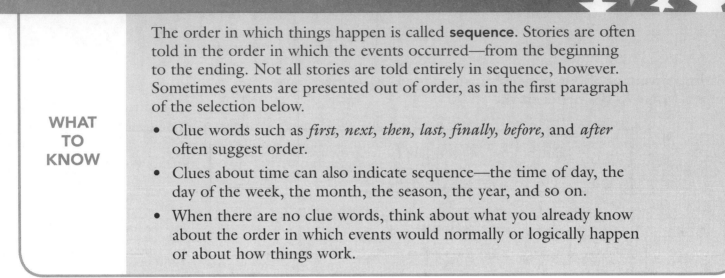

WHAT TO KNOW

The order in which things happen is called **sequence**. Stories are often told in the order in which the events occurred—from the beginning to the ending. Not all stories are told entirely in sequence, however. Sometimes events are presented out of order, as in the first paragraph of the selection below.

- Clue words such as *first, next, then, last, finally, before,* and *after* often suggest order.

- Clues about time can also indicate sequence—the time of day, the day of the week, the month, the season, the year, and so on.

- When there are no clue words, think about what you already know about the order in which events would normally or logically happen or about how things work.

**Read this selection from the first chapter of the science-fiction novel
Overlord of the Earth by Lloyd Arthur Eshbach. As you read, think
about the order in which things happen in the story.**

Kerry Kord crouched in utter blackness, sensing rather than seeing the other eighteen men in the belly of the glider. Only Glenn Bodey, squatting at his back, strapped with him in the two-man parachute, could he definitely identify. Minutes before, the motor of the giant tow-plane had been killed, and Kerry knew that the fleet of twenty-five gliders must be in the vicinity of the Overlord's Throne.

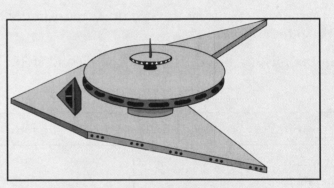

Inhaling deeply, Kerry touched the emergency 'chute release with his left hand and his Ghormley automatic with his right. A matter of minutes now. Despite rigid self-control, he could feel his heartbeat quicken, and a constriction high in his chest made breathing difficult. He rose to his full six-foot height; felt Glenn's broad form rising with him.

"Cold up here," the latter growled heavily. "I could do with a little heat."

"It'll be warmer shortly," Kerry commented. "Much warmer, very shortly."

The order in which things happen in the story is

The motor of the tow-plane was killed, or shut off.

Kerry Kord crouched in utter blackness.

Kerry inhaled deeply and touched the emergency parachute release.

Kerry and Glenn stood up inside the glider.

Read the next part of the story. As you read, ask yourself, "What happens first? What happens next?" Then answer the questions.

Momentarily, a red light winked over the heads of the waiting men: the signal. A rustle of synthane swished through the silence. Then a great door slid aside in the wall of the glider, and a blast of frigid air whipped through the opening.

"Jump position!" Kerry barked. "Two and two. Remember your instructions." He talked to fill in the gap before the actual leap into the dark. "We'll try to land on the flying field in front of the Star Tower. If we miss it, we get there as fast as we can. We join the wedge that blasts its way into the tower, and then we head for the top of the tower, blasting everything before us."

Kerry's words came faster. Time was running out. "If I get mine, Glenn takes over. If he goes, Gill is in command. If Gill goes—you know the order. Only get through!"

Again that flash of red! And the first pair of men leaped into the night. On the heels of the first, the second pair—the third—split seconds between jumps, the cords attached to the rod overhead automatically opening the 'chutes. Kerry and Glenn took their place in the line, the last to jump, save the pilot, who would abandon the glider and follow.

With a rush of thin, icy air, Kerry and his partner plummeted toward the Himalayan plateau far below.

1. What happened after the red light flashed the second time?

 Ⓐ The door of the glider slid open.

 Ⓑ The men got into jump position.

 Ⓒ The first pair of men leaped from the glider.

 Ⓓ Kerry repeated the men's instructions.

2. Which clue word tells when Kerry and Glenn jumped from the glider?

 Ⓐ first

 Ⓑ last

 Ⓒ before

 Ⓓ after

Work with a Partner

- Talk about your answers to the questions.
- Tell why you chose your answers.
- Then talk about what you have learned so far about understanding sequence.

> **REVIEW**
>
> Sequence is the order in which things are done or events happen.
>
> - Look for clue words that suggest order, such as *first, next, then, last, finally, before,* and *after.*
> - Look for clues that tell about time, such as the time of day, the day of the week, the month, the season, and the year.
> - When there are no clue words, think about the order in which things happen.

Read this science article which describes the five steps in the soil cycle. As you read, think about the clue words that tell the order of the steps. Then answer the questions.

The Soil Cycle

Soil is a mixture of inorganic and organic materials—rock and minerals, as well as decaying animal and plant matter. The soil cycle explains how soil stays healthy by the recycling of nutrients in soil with the help of plants. Plants are key to the soil cycle.

During the warm months, the air, water, and nutrients in the soil promote plant growth. As water seeps into the ground, it breaks down soil particles, releasing nutrients. The nutrients remain dissolved in the water. Plants then absorb the nutrient-enriched water through their roots and grow new leaves.

When plants become dormant in the cold months, the leaves fall to the soil. This plant litter builds up and begins to decompose. Next, soil animals like beetles and earthworms eat the plant litter and digest it in their body. Finally, the animals' waste, called castings, becomes nutrients for the soil. The castings mix with soil to create humus, the nutrient-rich soil ideal for crops.

The soil cycle begins again, and new plant growth takes place in the soil. This way, the soil stays healthy, and plants can continue to grow. Humans can't survive without plants, so we can't survive without soil either!

3. Which of these steps happens second in the soil cycle?
   - Ⓐ Leaves fall to the soil and begin to rot.
   - Ⓑ Soil animals digest the leaves, turning them into humus.
   - Ⓒ Water releases nutrients in the soil.
   - Ⓓ Plants absorb nutrients and grow new leaves.

4. Which clue word indicates the fourth step in the soil cycle?
   - Ⓐ next
   - Ⓑ then
   - Ⓒ last
   - Ⓓ finally

Which Answer Is Correct and Why?

Look at the answer choices for each question.
Read why each answer choice is correct or not correct.

3. **Which of these steps happens second in the soil cycle?**

   Ⓐ **Leaves fall to the soil and begin to rot.**

   This answer is not correct because it describes the third step in the soil cycle, not the second step.

   Ⓑ **Soil animals digest the leaves, turning them into humus.**

   This answer is not correct because it describes the fourth step in the soil cycle.

   Ⓒ **Water releases nutrients in the soil.**

   This answer is not correct because it describes the first step in the soil cycle.

   ● **Plants absorb nutrients and grow new leaves.**

   This answer is correct because it describes the second step in the soil cycle. The last sentence of paragraph 2 states that *"Plants then absorb the nutrient-enriched water through their roots and grow new leaves."*

4. **Which clue word indicates the fourth step in the soil cycle?**

   ● **next**

   This answer is correct because the clue word *next* begins the sentence in paragraph 3 that describes the fourth step in the soil cycle: *"Next, soil animals like beetles and earthworms eat the plant litter and digest it in their body."*

   Ⓑ **then**

   This answer is not correct because the clue word *then* indicates the second step in the soil cycle.

   Ⓒ **last**

   This answer is not correct because the clue word *last* is not found in this article.

   Ⓓ **finally**

   This answer is not correct because the clue word *finally* indicates the fifth step in the soil cycle. It is used at the beginning of the sentence in paragraph 3 that describes this step: *"Finally, the animals' waste, called castings, becomes nutrients for the soil."*

MORE TO KNOW	• Works of fiction, such as novels and short stories, often contain clue words or time clues to indicate sequence. • Works of nonfiction, such as articles and directions, often contain steps or time lines to indicate sequence.

Read this passage from a history of West Africa. Then answer the questions.

Kingdoms of Salt and Gold

From about 300 to 1600 A.D., many small kingdoms rose and fell in West Africa on grasslands between the Sahara and the southern forests. This region is called the Western Sudan. Three kingdoms—Ancient Ghana, Mali, and Songhay—became large empires. The unique geography of the Western Sudan provided sources of salt and gold and gave these kingdoms great wealth and power.

To the south of the grasslands, in the forests, were rich gold mines. But the South lacked salt, which was as valuable as gold. To the north, in the Sahara, were vast salt mines. As a result, prosperous trade arose between gold merchants and salt merchants. Numerous trade routes sprang up across the Sahara, through the grasslands and into the forests.

Camel caravans of Muslim traders from the North picked up salt. They next traveled for months to reach a centrally located market town, such as Timbuktu, in the Western Sudan. West African gold merchants traveled south to trade with the miners for gold, and then north to the market town. Traders met there and exchanged gold and salt.

In some cases, trading was conducted without words. Salt traders laid out their salt, beat drums to announce the trading, and then withdrew. Gold traders came forward, checked the salt, and set out the amount of gold they would pay. Salt traders returned to see if the price was right. If not, they beat drums again to signal a second round of trade.

5. The boxes show some of the things described in the passage.

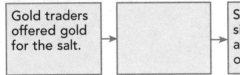
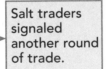

Gold traders offered gold for the salt. → [ ] → Salt traders signaled another round of trade.

What belongs in the empty box?
- Ⓐ Salt traders beat drums to announce trading.
- Ⓑ Gold traders made another offer.
- Ⓒ Salt traders decided whether to accept the offer.
- Ⓓ Gold traders checked the salt.

6. From which direction had Muslim traders originally traveled on their way to centrally located market towns?
- Ⓐ south
- Ⓑ north
- Ⓒ east
- Ⓓ west

7. Before they traded with the salt traders, gold merchants traded with
- Ⓐ Muslim traders of the North.
- Ⓑ gold miners of the South.
- Ⓒ merchants of Timbuktu.
- Ⓓ nomads of the Sahara.

8. Which clue word tells what Muslim traders did after they picked up their salt?
- Ⓐ before
- Ⓑ after
- Ⓒ finally
- Ⓓ next

Read this posting from the website of a middle school. Then answer the questions.

Eisenhower Middle School Presents
Third Annual Career-Exploration Day!

Saturday, January 21 • 8:00 A.M. – 4:00 P.M.
Some of the careers you can explore:
Astronaut, Building Contractor, Computer Programmer, Doctor, Website Designer, Lawyer, Medical Technician, Paralegal, Reporter, Veterinarian

8:00 A.M.–8:45 A.M.	Guest speaker: Dr. Rosalyn Jenkins, career counselor
9:00 A.M.–12:00 P.M.	Morning sessions: Six 30-minute presentations by professionals in various careers. See your program for the schedule of each career presentation.
12:15 P.M.–12:45 P.M.	Lunch served in the cafeteria.
1:00 P.M.–3:00 P.M.	Afternoon sessions: Four 30-minute presentations by professionals in various careers. See your program for the schedule of each career presentation.
3:15 P.M.–4:00 P.M.	Informal question-and-answer session. Meet the professionals one-on-one, and enjoy refreshments in the cafeteria.

Register for the Career Day now! Many students were turned away last year.
Sign up in the learning center, and receive the presentation schedule.
No charge for the day, due to sponsorship by the Parent Teacher Organization. Thank you, PTO!

9. The sentences below describe some of the events planned for Career Day.
   1. Students meet the professionals one-on-one.
   2. Lunch is served in the cafeteria.
   3. Professionals give their morning presentations.
   4. Dr. Jenkins speaks to the students.

   What is the correct order of the sentences?
   Ⓐ 1, 2, 3, 4   Ⓒ 4, 3, 2, 1
   Ⓑ 1, 3, 4, 2   Ⓓ 4, 2, 3, 1

10. Which event will happen fourth during Career Day?
    Ⓐ closing comments
    Ⓑ lunch will be served
    Ⓒ informal question-and-answer session
    Ⓓ afternoon sessions

11. Clues that tell about the sequence are
    Ⓐ times of day.
    Ⓑ days of the week.
    Ⓒ the words *first*, *next*, and *then*.
    Ⓓ dates, in years.

12. How many career presentations are scheduled for the morning session?
    Ⓐ one
    Ⓑ six
    Ⓒ four
    Ⓓ eight

Read another selection from *Overlord of the Earth*. Then answer questions about the selection. Choose the best answer for Numbers 13 and 14.

Curiously, Kerry peered into the sky around him. As far as the eye could see, he and Glenn were alone in the blackness. So perfectly were the others concealed, Kerry could not see them floating through the frigid air. He thought, "I must not fail."

In his mind's eye, Kerry saw again the final assembly of The Remnant—the comparative few of all mankind who refused to yield to Andrev, the Overlord, and had chosen instead to live almost as beasts among the ruins of once mighty cities. He saw again the close-packed, waiting thousands facing the high platform upon which had [stiffly] stood the Chief, Jonathan Hardinger, in the trim gray synthane of The Remnant. Behind him had sat The Ten, the scientists, councilors, and strategists of The Remnant. All about the platform, in motionless rank upon rank, arranged with military precision, had stood five hundred men in lusterless black—Kerry Kord among them.

He heard again the final ringing words of the Chief. "We need not die—and shall not die! Men will again be free!" Jonathan Hardinger's hand had indicated the ranks of the men in black. "Upon these men falls the greater task of the destruction of the Overlord himself. They are the pick of The Remnant, and they shall not fail!"

13. From the perspective of the storyteller, most of the events in the selection occur in

Ⓐ the present.

Ⓑ the future.

Ⓒ the past.

Ⓓ Kerry's mind.

14. The boxes show some of the things that happened in the selection.

Kerry peered out at the blackness.		Kerry saw again the final assembly.	Kerry heard again the Chief's final words.
1	2	3	4

What belongs in box 2?

Ⓐ Kerry thought he must not fail.

Ⓑ Kerry stood with The Remnant.

Ⓒ The Chief stood on the platform.

Ⓓ The Remnant refused to give up.

Read this biography about Wilma Mankiller, a Cherokee leader. Then answer questions about the biography. Choose the best answer for Numbers 15 and 16.

Leader of the Cherokee

In 1945, Wilma Mankiller was born on the family farm in Stilwell, Oklahoma. In 1957, the farm failed after two years of drought. Wilma's family then relocated to San Francisco. The family still struggled. But Wilma went on to graduate from high school, attend college, and become a social worker.

As a young adult, Wilma Mankiller worked to help the Pit River tribe of California. This experience led her to work on behalf of the Cherokee. She returned to the family farm in the mid-1970s. There, Mankiller began working to rebuild the Cherokee Nation. She organized programs to build and renovate homes, as well as to improve water systems.

Wilma Mankiller was elected deputy principal chief in 1983. She created new programs to establish small businesses. Income to the tribe increased. When the principal chief resigned in 1985, Mankiller became principal chief.

In spite of objection from some tribal leaders, Mankiller was elected principal chief in 1987. She improved employment, education, and health care. She also founded the Institute for Cherokee Literacy, to preserve language and traditions. Mankiller was reelected principal chief in 1991 and served the Cherokee Nation until 1995.

Wilma Mankiller did not seek reelection. But she did continue in her public role by writing and giving speeches across the country.

---

15. Which of these events happened first?

Ⓐ Wilma Mankiller began rebuilding the Cherokee Nation.

Ⓑ Wilma Mankiller was elected principal chief.

Ⓒ Wilma Mankiller worked to help the Pit River tribe.

Ⓓ Wilma Mankiller was elected deputy principal chief.

16. Which of these did Wilma Mankiller accomplish when she was principal chief?

Ⓐ She founded the Institute for Cherokee Literacy.

Ⓑ She established small businesses.

Ⓒ She organized community development.

Ⓓ She became a social worker.

Read this retelling of a Hawaiian folktale. Then answer questions about the folktale. Choose the best answer for Numbers 1 through 6.

Long ago, the King of Sharks saw a beautiful woman swimming skillfully along the shore. He fell in love with the woman and followed her to her village. There he changed himself into a handsome chief wearing a feathered cape, and he walked into the village.

The people of the village were honored that a chief from another land had come to visit them. They put together an enormous luau, and the people danced, feasted, and played games until late into the night. All night long, the King of Sharks won every game he played, and as the night drew to a close, he asked the beautiful woman to marry him. The woman was delighted to say yes to such a handsome and clever chief.

The two were married the next day, and the King of Sharks and his wife moved into a house next to a deep lagoon. In his human form, the King of Sharks swam every day in the deep blue waters of the lagoon. Soon the couple had a son, whom they named Nanave. A few years after Nanave was born, the King of Sharks returned to the ocean and was never seen in the village again. But before he left, he gave his young son the feathered cape and told the boy to wear it always to hide the mark of a shark on his back. Always loyal, the son promised to do as his father told him.

As the boy grew to manhood, every morning he would stand beside the deep lagoon, the feathered cape draped across his back. He would casually ask the passing fishermen where they were going to fish that day. The fishermen always told the friendly boy where they planned to go. Then Nanave would dive into the lagoon and disappear for the rest of the day.

Over time, the people of the village became hungrier and hungrier because the fishermen were catching fewer and fewer fish. The chief of the village called the people together and said, "Something bad is happening—it seems someone in our village is telling the sharks where we go to fish."

Nanave became frightened that the villagers would figure out that he was to blame, and he ran away from the crowd. He had gone only a few steps, however, when he slipped on some wet leaves and fell to the ground. His cape slipped off his shoulders, and the villagers could see on his back a shape that looked like a shark's mouth. Then the people knew that Nanave was loyal only to the sharks. They chased Nanave out of the village to the banks of the deep lagoon. Nanave jumped into the lagoon and swam out to sea to join his father, the King of the Sharks.

Ever since that day, Hawaiian fishermen have never told anyone where they intend to fish, for they fear that the sharks will overhear the plans and chase away the fish.

Finding Main Idea

1. The main idea of this story is found
   - Ⓐ in the first paragraph.
   - Ⓑ in the middle of the story.
   - Ⓒ in the last paragraph.
   - Ⓓ by thinking about the most important idea in the story.

Finding Main Idea

2. Which of these best explains the main idea of paragraph 6?
   - Ⓐ Nanave slipped on some wet leaves and fell to the ground.
   - Ⓑ Nanave's marked was revealed, and the villagers chased him out of the village.
   - Ⓒ Nanave became frightened of the villagers.
   - Ⓓ Nanave decided to jump into the lagoon and join his father, the King of the Sharks.

Recalling Facts and Details

3. How did the King of Sharks first appear to the beautiful woman?
   - Ⓐ as a chief
   - Ⓑ as a shark
   - Ⓒ as a fisherman
   - Ⓓ as a king

Recalling Facts and Details

4. Nanave ran away from the crowd because
   - Ⓐ he was frightened that the villagers would know he was to blame.
   - Ⓑ he wanted to catch fish for his dinner.
   - Ⓒ he wanted to hide the mark on his back.
   - Ⓓ he wanted the people to know he was loyal to the sharks.

Understanding Sequence

5. The boxes show some of the things that happened in the story.

The King of Sharks and the beautiful woman got married.	→		→	The King of Sharks was returned to the ocean and was never seen again.

   What belongs in the empty box?
   - Ⓐ The King of Sharks disguised himself as a handsome chief.
   - Ⓑ Nanave swam out to the sea to join his father.
   - Ⓒ Nanave was born.
   - Ⓓ Nanave ran from the villagers.

Understanding Sequence

6. Every day, after Nanave asked the fishermen where they were going to fish,
   - Ⓐ Nanave draped the feathered cape across his back.
   - Ⓑ Nanave went back home and ate lunch with his mother.
   - Ⓒ Nanave dove into the lagoon and disappeared for the rest of the day.
   - Ⓓ Nanave stayed by the deep lagoon and watched the fishermen fish.

**Read this article about lighthouses. Then answer questions about the article.
Choose the best answer to Numbers 7 through 12.**

Lighthouses are built on harbors, islands, and beaches. They act as guideposts for ships at night or in a storm. Their bright beams inform sailors that land is near and warn them of dangerous rocks and reefs.

The ancient Egyptians were probably the first people to use light as a way to guide ships. They kindled fires on the tops of hills at night to help sailors determine their positions. They later built lighthouses that also used fire as their light source. The Egyptians built the tallest lighthouse ever constructed. This one lighthouse stood 400 feet tall and guided ships for about 1,500 years.

The Romans also built lighthouses at a number of ports. In A.D. 43, they built light towers on both sides of the English Channel. The light beam from these towers was made by using a combination of fire and mirrors to reflect and illuminate the flames.

Early American lighthouses used oil lamps as a source of light. The first lighthouse in America was the Boston Lighthouse on Brewster Island in Boston Harbor. The lighthouse was first lit in 1716, but it was destroyed by the British during the American Revolution. Another lighthouse was built on the site in 1783 and still stands today.

Lighthouse keepers operated these early lighthouses. The keepers lived with their families in or near the lighthouse. The lighthouse keeper's duties included lighting the oil lamps, polishing the reflecting mirrors, and cleaning soot off the windows. The lighthouse keeper also replaced the fuel, rescued shipwrecked sailors, and sometimes fired a warning cannon during periods of fog.

In 1822, a Frenchman named Augustin Fresnel invented the first modern lighthouse lens. This lens increased the intensity of the light from the lamps by using prisms. Prisms in the lens reflected and strengthened the light. In 1841, the Fresnel lens was installed in a lighthouse for the first time.

Lighthouses today use electric lamps to show their light. Many also use the Fresnel lens, which has been improved upon over the years. Today, a Fresnel lens can project light for 20 miles. Electric motors provide the power to revolve the lens as lights flash from the lighthouse. Sometimes, however, ships cannot see the flashing lights due to fog or bad weather. Because of that, lighthouses have bells or signals to warn ships. Some lighthouses use sealed-beam lamps. Sealed-beam lamps swing around like a searchlight. These lamps can be seen through rain, fog, and snow.

Today, most lighthouses are fully automated and do not need a lighthouse keeper. The United States Coast Guard has maintained all the lighthouses in the United States since 1939.

Finding Main Idea

7. Which of these states the main idea of paragraph 2?
   Ⓐ The Egyptians were probably the first to use light to guide ships.
   Ⓑ Fire was a common light source for most early lighthouses.
   Ⓒ Lighthouses act as guideposts for ships at night or in storms.
   Ⓓ Some lighthouses have lasted for over 1,000 years.

Finding Main Idea

8. The article tells mainly about
   Ⓐ the construction of lighthouses.
   Ⓑ the history of lighthouses.
   Ⓒ how lighthouses have improved over the years.
   Ⓓ the different lights used in lighthouses.

Recalling Facts and Details

9. What did early American lighthouses use as a light source?
   Ⓐ fire
   Ⓑ mirrors
   Ⓒ electric lamps
   Ⓓ oil lamps

Recalling Facts and Details

10. Which of these was not a duty of early American lighthouse keepers?
    Ⓐ replacing lenses
    Ⓑ replacing fuel
    Ⓒ rescuing sailors
    Ⓓ polishing mirrors

Understanding Sequence

11. The chart shows some of the events described in the article.

    | The tallest lighthouse was constructed. | → | | → | The Boston lighthouse was destroyed. |

    What belongs in the empty box?
    Ⓐ A lighthouse was built in Boston in 1783.
    Ⓑ A Frenchman invented a lighthouse lens.
    Ⓒ Light towers were built on both sides of the English Channel.
    Ⓓ Fires were lit on top of hills to help guide sailors.

Understanding Sequence

12. Which of these happened last?
    Ⓐ The Boston Lighthouse was first lit.
    Ⓑ The Coast Guard began maintaining all U.S. lighthouses.
    Ⓒ Romans built lighthouses at a number of ports.
    Ⓓ The Fresnel lens was installed in a lighthouse for the first time.

What Is Cause and Effect?

There is a reason for everything that happens. What happens is called the *effect*.
Why it happens is called the *cause*. You can find examples of causes and their effects
almost anywhere.

1 Write what happens when a car runs out of gas.

_____

_____

_____

_____

_____

2 Tell why this happens.

_____

_____

_____

_____

_____

Work with a Partner

- Take turns giving each other examples of cause and effect.
- You might say, "My legs ached because I climbed a steep hill." In each example,
  tell which part is the cause and which part is the effect.

How Do You Find Cause and Effect?

Many reading passages include examples of cause and effect. You can find causes and effects by thinking about what happens in a passage and why.

Read this passage about World War II. Think about things that happened and why they happened.

> During World War II, the army needed many materials, including rubber, metal, and food. Many children went without sneakers because there was no rubber. People could not buy washing machines or refrigerators because metal was scarce. Limits were put on purchasing butter, sugar, and coffee. The government wanted to be sure that there were enough of these staples available for the soldiers.

1. Let's find an example of cause and effect in the passage.

   What happened? Children had to go without sneakers.
   This is an effect.

   Why did this happen? It happened because there was no rubber available.
   This is the cause.

2. Let's find another example of a cause and its effect.
   Look at the chart below.
   The second box shows an effect.

3. Fill in the missing information in the first box to tell the cause of the effect.

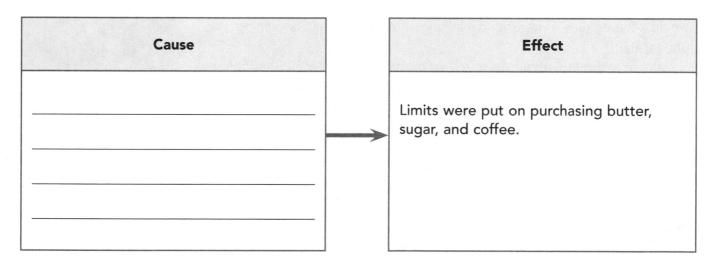

Cause		Effect
_____ _____ _____ _____	→	Limits were put on purchasing butter, sugar, and coffee.

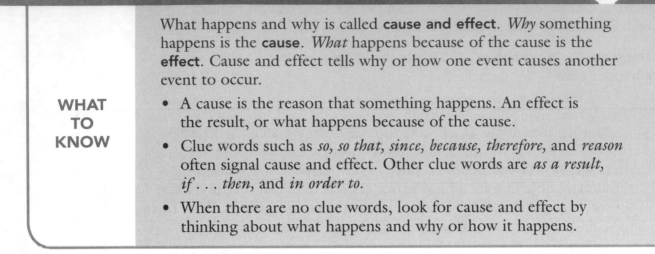

WHAT TO KNOW

What happens and why is called **cause and effect**. *Why* something happens is the **cause**. *What* happens because of the cause is the **effect**. Cause and effect tells why or how one event causes another event to occur.

- A cause is the reason that something happens. An effect is the result, or what happens because of the cause.

- Clue words such as *so, so that, since, because, therefore,* and *reason* often signal cause and effect. Other clue words are *as a result, if . . . then,* and *in order to.*

- When there are no clue words, look for cause and effect by thinking about what happens and why or how it happens.

Read this story about Jasmine. As you read, think about some of the things that happened in the story and why.

Jasmine's Problem

How would Jasmine solve this frustrating problem? Jasmine usually had no trouble solving her problems, but she was absolutely stumped by this one; she just couldn't figure out what to do about her friend Jessica. No matter what Jasmine tried, Jessica wouldn't stop talking to her during history class. Jasmine had tried many times to try to ignore her friend, but then Jessica's feelings would get hurt. Jasmine worried that, sooner or later, she or Jessica was going to get into trouble. Worse, Jasmine worried that her history grade would slip because of her friend's talking; the situation was becoming unbearable.

Jasmine thought about going to her history teacher, Mr. O'Shaughnessy, but she didn't want to get Jessica into trouble. So Jasmine decided to seek advice from someone else first. "A trusted adult would be best," she thought. "But who?" Jasmine decided to ask her older sister for help; maybe Claudia would know what to do.

Some of the things that happened in the story and why are:

What happened: **Jasmine had a problem.**
Why it happened: **Her friend wouldn't stop talking to her in class.**

What happened: **Jessica's feelings would get hurt.**
Why it happened: **Jasmine tried to ignore Jessica.**

What happened: **Jasmine decided not to talk to Mr. O'Shaughnessy.**
Why it happened: **She didn't want to get Jessica into trouble.**

Read this article about a unique breed of dog. As you read, look for clue words that will help you understand what happens and why.

When most people think of dalmatians, thoughts of fire engines and firefighters come to mind. Few people, however, know how the dalmatian became a popular resident at most fire stations.

Dalmatians are not fast dogs. However, they are able to run for long periods of time without rest. Dalmatians also have a natural ability to calm horses. In the 1700s, these dogs were used to protect the horses that pulled English stagecoaches. When other dogs tried to run out and frighten the horses, the dalmatians would chase the other dogs away. As a result, dalmatians formed a close bond with horses.

The dalmatian has been the firedog since fire departments first used horses to pull water pumpers to the scene of a fire. The dalmatian was kept in the firehouse to guard the firehouse and the horses. When an alarm came in, the dalmatian ran beside the horses until they reached the fire. They also prevented other dogs from interfering with the horses as they raced to the scene. Because the dalmatian has spots, it was easier for the horses to distinguish them from the other dogs. Once at the fire scene, dalmatians would continue to protect the horses from other animals.

Dalmatians were also used to protect the fire company's engine and equipment. There was a time when fire companies actually competed against each other at fire scenes. Different fire companies would try to outperform each other. Dalmatians would keep others from stealing or tampering with a fire company's equipment.

Over the years, there have been many stories about brave dalmatians rescuing trapped firefighters or victims. Today the dalmatian is the guard dog of the fire engine. In many areas, you can still see the dalmatian sitting at the back of the fire engine as it races to an emergency.

1. Why is it easy for horses to distinguish dalmatians from other dogs?
   - Ⓐ because dalmations are spotted
   - Ⓑ because dalmations are fast
   - Ⓒ because dalmations are small
   - Ⓓ because dalmations are brave

2. Which clue word or words in the article signal what happened because dalmations would chase other dogs away?
   - Ⓐ so
   - Ⓑ as a result
   - Ⓒ since
   - Ⓓ in order to

Work with a Partner

- Talk about your answers to the questions.
- Tell why you chose your answers.
- Then talk about what you have learned so far about recognizing cause and effect.

REVIEW

Cause and effect tells why or how one event causes another event to occur.

- To find a cause, look for *why* something happened. To find an effect, look for a result, or *what* happened.

- Look for clue words such as *so, so that, since, because, therefore, reason, as a result, if . . . then,* and *in order to.*

- When there are no clue words, think about what happened and why or how it happened.

Read this article about the first balloon flight. As you read, look for examples of cause and effect. Then answer the questions.

Joseph Michel and Jacques Étienne Montgolfier were brothers living in France in the 1700s. They shared the dream of flying. They hoped to build a hollow object that was light, yet strong enough to lift a large basket high into the sky. The basket would hold passengers, who could float over the earth, gazing with a bird's-eye view upon streets, fields, and rivers.

In order to rise, the hollow object would have to contain a gas that was lighter than air. The Montgolfiers knew about such a gas from recent scientific discoveries. It was created by mixing huge quantities of acid and metal. Today, we call this gas hydrogen.

The Montgolfiers tried using hydrogen in paper balloons, but the gas seeped out too easily. They then experimented with smoke. They burned various materials and let the smoke rise into the balloon. They believed that different kinds of smoke had different properties. If they found the right smoke, then it would have the special property to make the balloon rise. After many trials, they concluded that burning straw produced the right kind of smoke.

The Montgolfiers tested balloons of different sizes and materials. In June of 1783, they sent up into the sky a huge paper balloon weighing about three quarters of a ton. Filled with smoke from burning straw, the balloon rose more than a mile into the air before descending. The first balloon flight had been achieved!

3. What caused the paper balloon to rise?
   Ⓐ The balloon was extremely light.
   Ⓑ The balloon wasn't carrying anything heavy.
   Ⓒ The balloon was filled with smoke that had a special property.
   Ⓓ The balloon contained a gas that was heavier than air.

4. Which sentence contains an example of cause and effect?
   Ⓐ They hoped to build a hollow object that was light, yet strong enough to lift a large basket high into the sky.
   Ⓑ If they found the right smoke, then it would have the special property to make the balloon rise.
   Ⓒ They burned various materials and let the smoke rise into the balloon.
   Ⓓ The first balloon flight had been achieved!

Which Answer Is Correct and Why?

Look at the answer choices for each question.
Read why each answer choice is correct or not correct.

3. **What caused the paper balloon to rise?**

   Ⓐ **The balloon was extremely light.**

   This answer is not correct because in the last paragraph of the article, the paper balloon is described as being huge, *"weighing about three quarters of a ton."*

   Ⓑ **The balloon wasn't carrying anything heavy.**

   The answer is not correct because the article doesn't say whether the paper balloon was carrying anything at all.

   ● **The balloon was filled with smoke that had a special property.**

   This answer is correct because paragraph 3 states that *"If they found the right smoke, then it would have the special property to make the balloon rise."* The special property is explained earlier in the article, as *"a gas that was lighter than air."*

   Ⓓ **The balloon contained a gas that was heavier than air.**

   This answer is not correct because paragraph 2 explains that the hollow object must be filled with a gas lighter than air in order to rise.

4. **Which sentence contains an example of cause and effect?**

   Ⓐ **They hoped to build a hollow object that was light, yet strong enough to lift a large basket high into the sky.**

   This answer is not correct because, although this sentence points in the right direction, it does not indicate the main reason that the balloon would rise.

   ● **If they found the right smoke, then it would have the special property to make the balloon rise.**

   This answer is correct because the main reason that the balloon rose is explained in paragraph 2: *"In order to rise, the hollow object would have to contain a gas that was lighter than air."*

   Ⓒ **They burned various materials and let the smoke rise into the balloon.**

   This answer is not correct because it does not contain an example of cause and effect. It simply states some of the trials the brothers went through to find the right kind of smoke to make the balloon rise.

   Ⓓ **The first balloon flight had been achieved!**

   This answer is not correct because it is a statement that does not explain why or how the first balloon flight had been achieved, therefore it is not an example of cause and effect.

MORE TO KNOW	• A cause sometimes has more than one effect. • An effect sometimes has more than one cause. • Causes and effects are sometimes part of a chain of events. For example, one event (a cause) causes another event (an effect) to happen; then that event (which now becomes a cause) causes yet another event to happen (an effect).

Read this science article about sound waves. Then answer the questions.

Waves of Sound

Everyday life is full of sounds often taken for granted as part of our world. Have you ever considered how sound is created? Sound is a type of energy. It is produced when an object vibrates, or moves back and forth rapidly. This causes the air around the object also to vibrate. These vibrations travel as sound waves through the air. Sound waves are not visible to the eye; if you could perceive them, however, you would see spirals moving outward from the object like the rings of a metal coil.

When you ring a bell, the clapper strikes the metal of the bell and the metal vibrates. The vibrating metal of the bell causes the air around the bell to vibrate as well. These vibrations travel as sound waves in all directions through the air. When the sound waves reach your ears, you hear the ring of the bell.

Although sound waves are not visible, a device called an oscillator can measure sound. After the oscillator measures the sounds, the sound waves are depicted on a graph. The shape of the waves indicates certain qualities of sound. If the waves are close together, the sound is high-pitched—like the ring of the bell; if the waves are far apart, the sound is low-pitched—like the drone of a foghorn.

5. What causes the metal of a bell to vibrate?
   - (A) the ringing of the bell
   - (B) the clapper striking the bell
   - (C) the movement of the sound waves
   - (D) the pitch of the sound

6. What is the immediate result of the vibrations of the metal bell?
   - (A) The sound waves become visible.
   - (B) The bell becomes a metal coil.
   - (C) The air around the bell vibrates.
   - (D) The sound waves are produced.

7. When sound waves reach your ears,
   - (A) the sound waves stop traveling.
   - (B) the sound waves bounce off.
   - (C) you hear the sound of the ring.
   - (D) you cannot detect anything.

8. If the graph of sound waves shows waves that are far apart, then the sound is
   - (A) a bell.
   - (B) a foghorn.
   - (C) low-pitched.
   - (D) high-pitched.

44   Recognizing Cause and Effect

Read this article about runners. Then answer the questions.

Athletes in Action

The 100-meter sprint is the shortest race at an outdoor track-and-field competition. In the World Championship games, the winner of this race may well be called the fastest person in the world. Over the years, records in track-and-field events have continued to be broken. In the 100-meter sprint, a new record may be only one-hundredth of a second lower than the previous record. But new winners are still faster than ever. Why?

One important reason is science. About 100 years ago, a runner showed up for a race in Scotland. He got into a crouch for the start. The other runners laughed at him because no one had ever tried a crouch start before. But by starting low to the ground, the runner was putting more energy into forward motion than upward motion. He won the race. Soon the crouch became the standard position for the start of a short race.

The invention of video cameras and computers also made it possible for athletes to continue breaking records. A runner's performance is videotaped and fed into a computer. The computer program shows every movement. Sports scientists studying the movements might say, "If the runner makes a small change in arm position, she can reduce wind resistance. If she adjusts her body position in the starting blocks, she might cut two-hundredths of a second from her time." Computer analysis can make the difference between winning and losing.

9. One reason that new World Championship winners are faster than ever is
   - Ⓐ their improved attitude.
   - Ⓑ stronger competitors.
   - Ⓒ better nutrition.
   - Ⓓ the application of science.

10. The crouch position improves a runner's time because
   - Ⓐ the runner starts farther from the ground.
   - Ⓑ the runner puts more energy into forward motion.
   - Ⓒ the runner reduces air resistance.
   - Ⓓ the runner conserves more energy.

11. What effect can computer analysis have on a runner's performance?
   - Ⓐ It shows every movement the runner makes.
   - Ⓑ It can determine which starting position is best.
   - Ⓒ It can turn any runner into a world champion.
   - Ⓓ It can show minor adjustments that will improve performance.

12. Sports scientists might say that if a runner makes a small change in arm position,
   - Ⓐ she can run more comfortably.
   - Ⓑ she can adjust her body position in the starting blocks.
   - Ⓒ she can reduce wind resistance.
   - Ⓓ she can cut two-hundredths of a second from her time.

TEST TIPS	• A test question about cause and effect may ask you *what* happened (the effect) or *why* it happened (the cause).
	• A test question about cause and effect often contains words such as *because, why, reason, what happened,* or *as a result.*

Read this excerpt from a 1976 interview with a Slovakian immigrant who came to the United States in 1897. Then answer questions about the interview. Choose the best answer for Numbers 13 and 14.

You Want to Know

Q: Why did you come to this country?

A: You're interested in knowing why I came here, to America? Well, permit me to start at the beginning then. My name is Mary Sivulich, and I'm from the old country. I was born in 1883 on my family's farm in the Carpathian Mountains, part of what was the Austro-Hungarian Empire. I want to be clear—my accent always confuses people—we were Slovakian, not Russian.

Anyway, there were so many mouths to feed in my family that, as a child, I worked for my wealthy Jewish neighbor. I worked as her servant, but she was kindhearted and always treated me well. When I was fourteen, my neighbor offered to bring me along with her when she emigrated from our country to the United States. I'll never forget her kindness and generosity to me. Since I was unmarried and therefore something of a burden, my poor parents were glad to have me leave, so off I traveled across the ocean to America.

For the first four years, I lived with a family in Philadelphia, working as their maid and cook. I didn't mind at first; I was grateful to be in America. But as I got older, I longed for a life of my own. Then I met my husband, John, when he was passing through Philly. He worked on the railroad, building water towers when new lines of track were laid. At eighteen—I was already old!—I married John, and we moved to Chicago. There we built our life together. I had six children, and they didn't have to work until high school.

I never looked back, even when my parents wanted us to take over their farm back in the old country.

13. One reason that Mary's parents were glad she was leaving home was that Mary

   Ⓐ was very young.

   Ⓑ was not married.

   Ⓒ had a good job.

   Ⓓ was doing what she wanted.

14. Why did Mary eventually want to leave her job as a maid and cook?

   Ⓐ She wanted to return to her parents' farm.

   Ⓑ She wanted to get married as soon as possible.

   Ⓒ She wanted a life independent of her employer.

   Ⓓ She wanted a job in Chicago.

Read this biographical sketch about a brave First Lady. Then answer questions about the biographical sketch. Choose the best answer for Numbers 15 and 16.

A First Lady's Courage

Dolley Madison was one of the most beloved First Ladies ever to occupy the White House. She displayed a courage that was rare among many of Washington's residents.

During the War of 1812, the British were planning an attack on Washington. On August 22, 1814, President Madison set out for Bladensburg, Maryland. He needed to assess how well prepared the American troops were to defend that area. He instructed his wife, Dolley, to be ready on a moment's notice to leave the city. If he couldn't return in time to escape the city with her, she needed to be ready to leave without him.

Dolley Madison did not want to leave the city without her husband. She knew there was much hostility toward him and that he was in grave danger. She wanted to wait as long as possible for his return to the White House. While the First Lady waited, she packed a carriage with as many valuable objects as she could.

As news spread that the British were nearing Washington, the hundred men guarding the White House fled. Dolley Madison spent the night of August 23 alone, except for a few loyal servants. By the next day, she could hear cannons firing in the distance. Horsemen galloped down Pennsylvania Avenue warning everyone to flee. But the First Lady insisted on saving the portrait of the first president before she left.

When Dolley Madison finally did flee the city, she met up with her husband in a nearby tavern. Together, from a safe distance, they watched as Washington burned. Because of Dolley Madison, the United States still has the famous portrait of George Washington that hangs in the East Room of the White House today.

15. What was the effect of Dolley Madison's actions?

Ⓐ Many valuable objects were saved.

Ⓑ The city of Washington was saved.

Ⓒ People decided to stay in the city and fight.

Ⓓ The British turned back at the last minute.

16. The graphic organizer shows a cause-and-effect relationship.

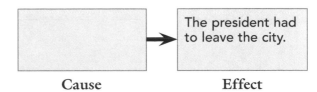

Cause	Effect

What belongs in the empty box?

Ⓐ President Madison had to assess the area's defenses.

Ⓑ President Madison's life was in danger.

Ⓒ President Madison needed to fight against British troops.

Ⓓ President Madison saw that the British had burned Washington.

COMPARING AND CONTRASTING

PART ONE: Think About the Strategy

What Is Comparing and Contrasting?

Thinking about the ways two or more things are alike is *comparing*.
Thinking about the ways two or more things are different is *contrasting*.
You can compare and contrast almost anything.

1 Write how a butterfly and a bird are alike.

_____

_____

_____

_____

_____

2 Write how a butterfly and a bird are different.

_____

_____

_____

_____

_____

Work with a Partner

- Take turns telling each other something that is the same about two things, such as animals, sports, or objects.
- Then tell something that is different about these things. See how many likenesses and differences you can find.

How Do You Find Likenesses and Differences?

Many reading passages compare and contrast two or more things. You can find examples of comparing and contrasting by thinking about the details you read.

Read this passage about small farms in the past and large farms in the present. Think about how they are similar and how they are different.

> Not very long ago, most farms were small and family owned. Crops were grown to provide for the family and to supply food to people in other parts of the country. Today, most farms are larger and are owned by big businesses. They grow more crops and are able to supply food to even more people, around the world. There are few family farms that can afford to compete against these large farms. Many small family farms have been forced out of business while the large farms thrive.

1. Let's think about the details that tell about the likenesses between small farms run by families and large farms run by big businesses.

   Now think about the details that tell about the differences between them.

2. Look at the Venn diagram below.

   The shaded part of the first circle tells how small farms are different from large farms. The shaded part of the second circle tells how large farms are different from small farms. These are examples of *contrasting*.

   The overlapping information tells how both kinds of farms are alike. This is *comparing*.

3. Fill in the missing information in the overlapping part, giving another example of comparing.

4. Fill in the missing information in the shaded part of the second circle, giving another example of contrasting.

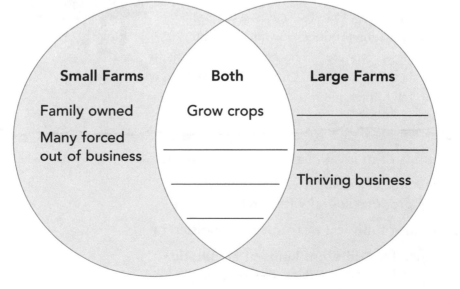

Small Farms

Family owned

Many forced out of business

Both

Grow crops

_____

_____

_____

Large Farms

_____

_____

Thriving business

WHAT TO KNOW

Finding how two or more things are alike and how they are different is called **comparing and contrasting**. A comparison tells how things, people, places, or events are alike. A contrast tells how they are different.

- Comparing is finding how two or more things are alike. Contrasting is finding how two or more things are different.

- Clue words that signal a comparison are *both, same, like, alike,* and *similar.* Clue words that signal a contrast are *but, unlike, different, however, whereas,* and *instead.*

- If there are no clue words in a reading passage to signal a comparison or a contrast, think about the things you read about. Ask yourself, "How are these things alike? How are they different?"

Read this article about the kinds of sound musical instruments make. As you read, think about the ways these sounds are similar and the ways they are different.

Musical instruments make a variety of sounds—loud, soft, high, and low. The loudness or softness of a sound is called amplitude. The amplitude of sound produced by a musical instrument depends upon how hard it is blown, struck, plucked, or bowed. If a musical instrument is played lightly, it sounds soft. However, if the same instrument is played heavily, it sounds loud. Take the drum. If you strike the drum with a light touch, you will hear a soft, gentle tap; but if you strike it forcefully, you will hear a loud, thundering boom.

In addition to loud and soft, the sounds of a musical instrument may be high or low. The highness or lowness of a sound is called pitch. Most instruments make many sounds with a certain pitch. Musical sounds with a certain pitch are more commonly known as notes. Different musical instruments produce sounds with a different range of pitch—that is, a different set of notes. Generally, a tuba produces low-pitched notes, whereas a flute produces high-pitched notes. Some instruments are not limited in this way. The piano, for example, creates a wide range of notes from low pitch to high pitch.

Ways in which the sounds of musical instruments are similar:

All musical instruments produce sounds with amplitude.
All musical instruments produce sound with pitch.

Ways in which the sounds of musical instruments are different:

Different instruments produce different kinds of amplitude.
Different instruments produce different ranges of pitch.

Read this article about work. As you read, look for clue words that signal similarities and differences between a career and a job. Then answer the questions.

Is It a Career or a Job?

We often use the words *career* and *job* to discuss the same thing—work—but there is a difference between these two words. A career usually refers to the course or path of one's working life, while a job is just one part of the journey. In more practical terms, a career is a profession or an occupation. A job is a position of employment. For example, food services is a career, whereas grill cook is a job. Ideally, one can choose from many jobs within a career. But having this kind of choice requires preparation. It's never too early to begin thinking about and researching the kind of career you want.

Think carefully about a career path. You most likely will spend forty to fifty years of your life working, so personal satisfaction is essential. Get as much information as you are able about the career in which you are interested. What level of education do you need to enter and then advance in this career? Learn about the outlook of the career. What types of jobs will be available after you complete your education? There are many places to find information, including books, career or job fairs, interviews with family members or friends, and volunteer work.

1. What is one difference between a career and a job?

    Ⓐ A career is a position, but a job is a profession.

    Ⓑ A career is satisfying, but a job is essential.

    Ⓒ A career is a profession, but a job is a position of employment.

    Ⓓ A career requires education, but a job does not.

2. Which clue word signals the difference between food services and grill cook?

    Ⓐ different

    Ⓑ whereas

    Ⓒ same

    Ⓓ alike

Work with a Partner

- Talk about your answers to the questions.
- Tell why you chose your answers.
- Then talk about what you have learned so far about comparing and contrasting.

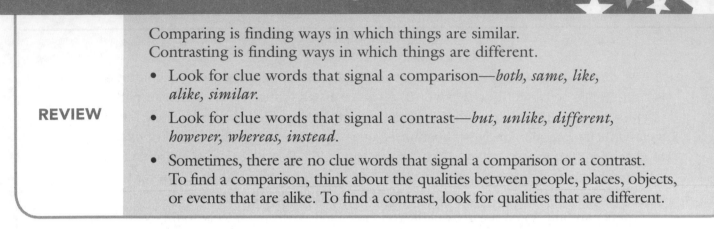

REVIEW

Comparing is finding ways in which things are similar.
Contrasting is finding ways in which things are different.

- Look for clue words that signal a comparison—*both, same, like, alike, similar.*

- Look for clue words that signal a contrast—*but, unlike, different, however, whereas, instead.*

- Sometimes, there are no clue words that signal a comparison or a contrast. To find a comparison, think about the qualities between people, places, objects, or events that are alike. To find a contrast, look for qualities that are different.

Read this article about meteors and meteorites. As you read, ask yourself, "How are meteors and meteorites alike? How are they different?" Then answer the questions.

Many people think that meteors and meteorites are the same natural phenomena. Many people refer to meteors and meteorites as "shooting stars." However, meteors and meteorites are not stars at all. Both meteors and meteorites share a common origin, but each has its own qualities.

Meteors are small particles of dust, left behind by a comet's tail. When these particles of dust enter the earth's atmosphere, they burn up before reaching the ground. In the night sky, meteors appear as streaks of light. Showers of meteors are visible several times a year.

Meteorites are large particles of rock and metal from a comet that has broken up. Meteorites crash through the earth's atmosphere without burning up, and they strike the ground intact. Meteorites usually have little effect, but this depends upon their size and location. Occasionally, they destroy property or leave a crater in the earth's surface.

3. What is one way meteors and meteorites are similar?

- Ⓐ They both can be found on the earth's surface.
- Ⓑ They both cause little damage to the earth.
- Ⓒ They both have a common origin.
- Ⓓ They both fall through the sky in showers.

4. Which clue word signals this similarity between meteors and meteorites?

- Ⓐ but
- Ⓑ instead
- Ⓒ alike
- Ⓓ both

Which Answer Is Correct and Why?

**Look at the answer choices for each question.
Read why each answer choice is correct or not correct.**

3. **What is one way meteors and meteorites
are similar?**

Ⓐ **They both can be found on
the earth's surface.**

This answer is not correct because
the article states that only meteorites
can enter through the atmosphere
and hit the surface of the earth.

Ⓑ **They both cause little damage
to the earth.**

This answer is not correct because,
according to the article, a meteorite can
occasionally cause damage on the earth.
The article states that meteors burn up
before reaching the ground.

🔴 **They both have a common origin.**

This answer is correct because this
similarity is partially stated in the last
sentence of the first paragraph: *"Both
meteors and meteorites share a common
origin . . ."* The definition of meteors
in paragraph 2 and the definition of
meteorites in paragraph 3 further explain
this origin to readers.

Ⓓ **They both fall through the sky
in showers.**

This answer is not correct because
the article only states that meteors
fall through the sky in showers.

4. **Which clue word signals this similarity
between meteors and meteorites?**

Ⓐ **but**

This answer is not correct because the clue
word *but* usually indicates a difference.

Ⓑ **instead**

This answer is not correct because the clue
word *instead* usually indicates a difference.

Ⓒ **alike**

This answer is not correct because the clue
word *alike* does not appear in the article.

🔴 **both**

This answer is correct because the clue
word *both* is used at the end of the first
paragraph to signal the similarity
between meteors and meteorites.

MORE TO KNOW

Sometimes, there are no clue words in a reading passage to signal that things are being compared or contrasted. When there are no clue words,

- think about the people, places, objects, or events that you read about. Ask yourself, "How are they alike? How are they different?"
- think about what is being compared or contrasted. Ask yourself, "In what ways are they compared? In what ways are they contrasted?"
- look for metaphors or similes. Writers use them to compare two unlike things.

Read this article about the Olympics and the X games. Then answer the questions.

Let the Games Begin!

Contests of strength, speed, and skill have always attracted audiences. The first Olympic games took place in ancient Greece. The modern Olympics began in 1896. Nearly a century later, the first X Games took place in 1995.

The Olympics and its rookie counterpart, the X Games, are international athletic competitions. In both, talented athletes from different countries compete for gold, silver, and bronze medals. Medalists in the X Games also receive prize money.

The Olympic games and the X Games are held in winter and in summer. The Olympics take place every two years in different host cities around the world. The X Games are played every year in the United States.

At the Olympics, athletes compete in traditional sports. The summer games include track-and-field events, basketball, and swimming. Figure skating and cross-country skiing are standards at the winter games.

Athletes at the X Games compete in extreme action sports. These daredevil sports hold a higher level of danger. For example, the X Games feature snowmobiling in winter. They include skateboarding and rally car racing in summer.

Several X Games sports have crossed over to the Olympics. Snowboarding is now an official event at the Winter Olympics. Bicycle motocross (BMX) has been introduced at the Summer Olympics. A number of athletes have competed in—and won medals at—both the Olympics *and* the X Games.

5. How are the Olympics and the X Games alike?
   - Ⓐ Both award gold, silver, and bronze medals.
   - Ⓑ Both take place every two years.
   - Ⓒ Both take place in host cities around the world.
   - Ⓓ Both began in the mid 1990s.

6. The Olympics differ from the X Games because they
   - Ⓐ attract fewer athletes.
   - Ⓑ are not held in winter months.
   - Ⓒ have a much longer history.
   - Ⓓ are played every year.

7. In the article, the X Games are compared to
   - Ⓐ a veteran.
   - Ⓑ a pinch hitter.
   - Ⓒ a rookie.
   - Ⓓ an all-star.

8. In what way are the X Games different from the Olympics?
   - Ⓐ The X Games have figure skating, but the Olympics do not.
   - Ⓑ The X Games have snowboarding, but the Olympics do not.
   - Ⓒ The X Games have snowmobiling, but the Olympics do not.
   - Ⓓ The X Games have basketball, but the Olympics do not.

**Read this article about disposable and reusable grocery bags.
Then answer the questions.**

What's Your Bag?

Do you carry groceries in disposable bags that are thrown away after one use? Or do you carry groceries in a reusable bag to be used multiple times? Both kinds of bags have benefits and drawbacks.

Disposable plastic and paper bags are lightweight. They can be recycled, or they can be reused around the home. For example, plastic bags can line trash cans, and paper bags can cover textbooks.

Despite these advantages, most experts agree that disposable bags harm the environment. Sea turtles and other marine animals choke on plastic bags drifting in oceans. In landfills, recycled plastic bags take hundreds of years to break down. As plastic breaks down, it releases poisonous materials into the soil and water. And disposable paper bags are not faultless. Millions of trees are cut down annually to make paper bags. Making paper bags uses more energy and creates more pollution than making plastic bags does.

Reusable cloth, nylon, or canvas bags are better for the environment. They reduce waste and save energy. Compared to flimsy disposable bags, they are stronger, last longer, and hold more items. Unlike disposables, reusable bags come in different sizes, colors, and styles.

However, reusable bags have disadvantages. Whereas most disposable bags are free, reusable ones cost money. In addition, reusable bags are less convenient. They can be bulky to store, and they have to be washed. Also shoppers may forget to bring them to the supermarket.

9. According to this article, the use of reusable bags protects the environment, while the use of disposable bags

Ⓐ negatively affects the environment.

Ⓑ also protects the environment.

Ⓒ improves the environment.

Ⓓ has no impact on the environment.

10. How is the cost of reusable bags different from that of disposable bags?

Ⓐ Reusable bags do not cost any money.

Ⓑ Reusable bags cost more than disposable bags.

Ⓒ Reusable bags cost the same as disposable bags.

Ⓓ Reusable bags cost less than disposable bags.

11. In what way are reusable bags and disposable bags alike?

Ⓐ They both are free.

Ⓑ They both reduce waste.

Ⓒ They both can be used in grocery supermarkets.

Ⓓ They both are strong and sturdy.

12. One advantage reusable bags have that disposable bags do not have is that

Ⓐ reusable bags come in an assortment of styles and sizes.

Ⓑ reusable bags don't require any energy to produce.

Ⓒ reusable bags are made of lightweight paper or plastic.

Ⓓ reusable bags don't take up a lot of room.

- A test question about comparing and contrasting may ask you how things are alike or how they are different.
- A test question about comparing and contrasting usually contains a clue word. Words such as *alike, similar,* and *both* signal that you are to compare. Words such as *unlike* or *different* signal that you are to contrast.

Read this Celtic myth about the Morrigan. Then answer questions about the myth. Choose the best answer for Numbers 13 and 14.

Three Appearances of the Morrigan

Several Celtic myths about warriors feature the Morrigan, the war goddess. In one of these myths, the Morrigan appears to the hero, Cu Chulainn, at three different times in his life. Each time, Cu Chulainn fails to recognize her until it is too late, which eventually causes his doom.

The first time that the Morrigan appears to Cu Chulainn, she offers her love to him. She tells him that she has been aiding him in battle and will continue to do so. But, since he is in the midst of fighting a war, he refuses her love, saying he doesn't have the time for her and, besides, he doesn't need her help. Angered, the Morrigan vows to hinder him in battle instead. Cu Chulainn rushes at her with his sword. Just as the blade touches the Morrigan, she transforms into a crow and flies away. Only then does Cu Chulainn recognize her.

Later in his life, Cu Chulainn comes upon an old woman with several wounds who is milking a cow. He asks the old woman for a drink, which she gladly gives to him. In gratitude, he thanks her with a blessing. Upon receiving the blessing, her wounds are healed. Cu Chulainn continues on his way, without realizing that the old woman was the Morrigan and that he has healed the very wounds he had inflicted upon her years ago. Now the Morrigan's power is only greater.

At the end of his life, Cu Chulainn is visited by the Morrigan in the guise of a young woman washing his clothing and armaments at a river—for the Celts, a sign of coming death. Knowing he is about to face his enemies, Cu Chulainn feels overwhelmed by this sign. During the battle that follows, Cu Chulainn is severely wounded. When a crow lands on his shoulder, Cu Chulainn sees that it is the Morrigan and the hero dies quickly. The Morrigan has had her final victory.

13. How are Cu Chulainn's three encounters with the Morrigan alike?
   - Ⓐ He disrespects and mistreats her.
   - Ⓑ He recognizes her too soon.
   - Ⓒ He recognizes her every time.
   - Ⓓ He doesn't recognize her until it's too late.

14. What was most different about the Morrigan's second appearance as compared to the first and third appearances?
   - Ⓐ She is healthy and young.
   - Ⓑ She transforms into a crow.
   - Ⓒ She is a woman.
   - Ⓓ She does not transform into a crow.

Read this article about an infamous war from ancient times. Then answer questions about the article. Choose the best answer for Numbers 15 and 16.

In about 800 B.C., Greeks would gather in the town square to listen to a blind storyteller named Homer. As he sang of past heroes and their great deeds, the listeners learned about honor and courage. In a long, epic poem called *The Iliad*, Homer related the story of a war that ravaged the city of Troy hundreds of years before he lived. This infamous war was called the Trojan War. In *The Iliad*, Homer told that the people of Troy, the Trojans, defended their city against Greek attackers for ten years during the Trojan War.

Homer explained the events that led to the war this way. Paris, son of King Priam of Troy, kidnapped Helen, queen of the Greek city of Sparta and wife of King Menelaus. According to the gods, Helen was the most beautiful woman in the world. Even though she was already married, Paris brought Helen to Troy to be his wife. But history gives another cause for the war. The Trojans and the Greeks were rival sea traders. Each group wanted to trade freely along the rich sea routes linking Europe and Asia. Perhaps the Trojans forced the Greeks to pay a toll on their way past Troy to and from the Black Sea.

The Trojan War ended in about 1250 B.C. Homer explained that in the tenth year of the war, the Greek army thought of a clever plan to defeat the Trojans. Knowing the Trojans loved horses, the Greeks tricked them with the gift of a horse, the Trojan Horse. The Greek army pretended to give up and sail off, leaving behind a gigantic wooden horse outside the city walls. Curious, the Trojans rolled the horse into their city without realizing the body of the horse was packed with armed Greeks. At night, the Greek soldiers climbed down from the horse and unlocked the city gates for their waiting army. The Greek army flooded through the gates. This surprise attack allowed the Greeks to easily defeat the Trojans.

15. Homer attributes the cause of the Trojan War to a kidnapping, but history indicates that
    Ⓐ the Trojans attacked the Greeks, beginning the war.
    Ⓑ a Greek attack against the Trojans led to the war.
    Ⓒ a trade dispute probably caused the war.
    Ⓓ a family feud was responsible for the war.

16. In what way were the Greeks and the Trojans similar in their approach to the war?
    Ⓐ Both were fierce.
    Ⓑ Both were clever.
    Ⓒ Both were persistent.
    Ⓓ Both were untrained.

PART ONE: Think About the Strategy

What Is a Prediction?

A prediction is a good guess about something that will happen at a later time.
A prediction is based partly on information that you already know from your own experiences.
When you are making a prediction, it is important to think about the clues that help
you make your prediction, as well as what you already know.

1 Write the name of a TV show or movie for which you saw previews before
you watched it.

_____

_____

2 Write the clues you used to predict whether or not you would like the TV show
or movie.

_____

_____

_____

3 Was your prediction correct? Why or why not?

_____

_____

_____

Work with a Partner

- Take turns telling each other about something you thought would happen that actually
  did happen. You might tell about the outcome of a sporting event that you had
  predicted or about how your pets actually liked the new food that you had
  predicted they would like.

- Explain what made you think this thing would happen.

How Do You Make a Prediction?

You can make a prediction about a reading passage before you begin reading. Sometimes the title of the passage gives you a clue about what you will be reading.

Read this passage about Tam. See if you can figure out what will probably happen next.

The Determined Biker

Tam had been looking forward to this bike trip all week. But his outing seemed doomed from the start. He hadn't traveled more than one mile before a sudden rainstorm soaked his clothes. He stopped under a bridge until the rain stopped. Once the rain passed, he hadn't traveled more than one more mile before trouble struck again. Tam heard a loud pop, and his bike was suddenly difficult to steer. Tam shook his head at the flat tire, but there was only one thing for the determined biker to do.

---

1. This title tells something about the character in the passage. You could figure out from the title that the story would be about a biker who, for one reason or another, was determined.

2. Now let's think about what you read in the passage and make a prediction.

3. Look at the magnifying glass below. It shows the last sentence in the passage. See if you can predict what will happen next.

> **Tam shook his head at the flat tire, but there was only one thing for the determined biker to do.**

> Predictions:
>
> 1. Tam will fix the tire and continue on the trip.
>
> 2. Tam will walk home with his bike in tow.

4. The box next to the magnifying glass shows two predictions about what might happen next. The two predictions are very different. Only one is a good prediction, based on the passage.

5. Read the title and the whole passage again. Also think about what you already know.

6. Which prediction do you think is best? Write it on the lines below.

_____

_____

WHAT TO KNOW

When you think about what might happen next in a reading passage, you are **making a prediction**. Making a prediction is a way of using clues from a reading passage, as well as things you already know, to make a good guess about what might happen next.

- Clues are often in the title of a reading passage. You can use a title to make a prediction about what you will be reading.

- Clues are in the details in a reading passage. Details about the things characters do and say can help you make a prediction about what they might do or say later in a story.

- Clues are often in any pictures included with a passage. Pictures may show something that is happening or might happen soon.

- A good prediction combines passage clues with your own personal knowledge.

Read this story about Jackson and his practice for a piano recital. As you read, think about what might happen next in the story.

Jackson had practiced the piece for at least two hours every day since his piano teacher, Mrs. Wilcox, had informed him about the recital. It was a difficult work by Chopin, and Jackson was still having trouble with the trills. It was only three hours until the recital. Jackson's parents and his friends would be there to hear him play. The pressure was building up, and Jackson did not perform well under stress. Jackson continued working on the piece, paying particular attention to the trills. But the more he practiced, the worse he played. And now it was time to get ready for the recital.

Think about what you read and what you already know about the things that might happen when people are nervous. Make a good guess about what might happen next. Then, continue reading to see how close your guess is to what actually happens.

Jackson walked onto the stage, the knot in his stomach turning tighter. He didn't look out at the audience as he took his seat. His hands trembled above the keyboard, and there was no controlling them. Jackson took a deep breath and began. As he played, even Jackson knew his performance was not great. He couldn't wait to leave the stage.

What happened next in the story was that **Jackson did not perform well at the recital.**

Read the first part of this Japanese folktale. As you read, look for clues that will help you make predictions about what might happen. Ask yourself, "What does the title tell me about what I will be reading? Which details provide clues about what will probably happen?" Then answer the questions.

The Straw Millionaire

One day, an honorable and thoughtful young man named Shobei was in a temple praying to a god for good luck. The god told Shobei that the next thing he touched would belong to him. When Shobei left the temple, he tripped over a stone and fell to the ground. As he dusted himself off, he realized that he held a single strand of straw in his hand. He said to himself, "It doesn't seem like much, but the straw is mine," and he carefully put the strand away for safekeeping.

1. What will most likely happen next?
   A The straw will bring good fortune to Shobei.
   B The god will punish Shobci for keeping the straw.
   C Shobei will forget about the straw.
   D Bad luck will befall Shobei.

2. Where did you find clues to help you make your prediction?
   A in the title of the story
   B in the things that Shobei said
   C in the details about the temple
   D in the details about why Shobei tripped

Work with a Partner

- Talk about your answers to the questions.
- Tell why you chose your answers.
- Then talk about what you have learned so far about making predictions.

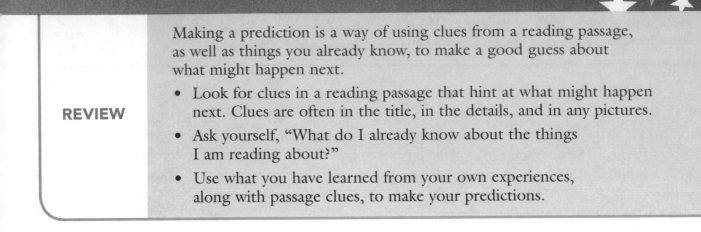

REVIEW

Making a prediction is a way of using clues from a reading passage, as well as things you already know, to make a good guess about what might happen next.

- Look for clues in a reading passage that hint at what might happen next. Clues are often in the title, in the details, and in any pictures.
- Ask yourself, "What do I already know about the things I am reading about?"
- Use what you have learned from your own experiences, along with passage clues, to make your predictions.

Read the rest of the folktale about Shobei. As you read, look for clues that will help you predict some of the things that will happen to Shobei. Then answer the questions.

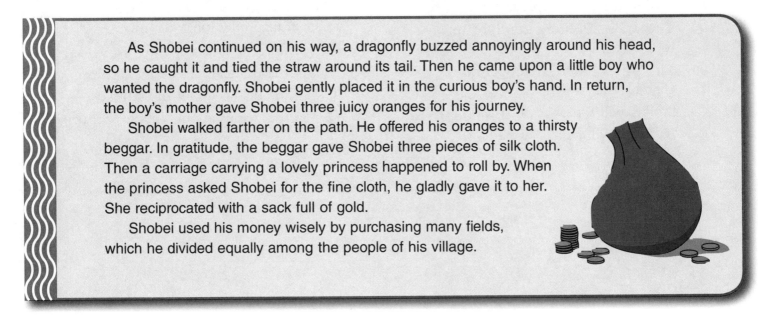

As Shobei continued on his way, a dragonfly buzzed annoyingly around his head, so he caught it and tied the straw around its tail. Then he came upon a little boy who wanted the dragonfly. Shobei gently placed it in the curious boy's hand. In return, the boy's mother gave Shobei three juicy oranges for his journey.

Shobei walked farther on the path. He offered his oranges to a thirsty beggar. In gratitude, the beggar gave Shobei three pieces of silk cloth. Then a carriage carrying a lovely princess happened to roll by. When the princess asked Shobei for the fine cloth, he gladly gave it to her. She reciprocated with a sack full of gold.

Shobei used his money wisely by purchasing many fields, which he divided equally among the people of his village.

3. Predict which of these will most likely happen.

Ⓐ Shobei will earn the respect of the villagers.

Ⓑ Shobei will cheat the villagers out of their property.

Ⓒ Shobei will become greedy for more wealth.

Ⓓ Shobei will request more gold from the princess.

4. Which detail from the folktale helped you make your prediction?

Ⓐ In return, the boy's mother gave Shobei three juicy oranges for his journey.

Ⓑ As Shobei continued on his way, a dragonfly buzzed annoyingly around his head, so he caught it and tied the straw around its tail.

Ⓒ Shobei used his money wisely by purchasing many fields, which he divided equally among the people of his village.

Ⓓ When the princess asked Shobei for the fine cloth, he gladly gave it to her.

Which Answer Is Correct and Why?

**Look at the answer choices for each question.
Read why each answer choice is correct or not correct.**

3. **Predict which of these will most likely happen.**

   ● **Shobei will earn the respect of the villagers.**

   This answer is correct because the story tells you that Shobei used his gold to purchase fields, which he divided equally among the people of the village. It is likely the people will respect Shobei for his generosity.

   Ⓑ **Shobei will cheat the villagers out of their property.**

   This answer is not correct because there is nothing about Shobei's behavior that would indicate that he is anything but generous. There is nothing in the story to indicate that his behavior would change.

   Ⓒ **Shobei will become greedy for more wealth.**

   This answer is not correct because Shobei behaved generously with others, sharing his good fortune. There is nothing in the story to indicate that his behavior would likely change.

   Ⓓ **Shobei will request more gold from the princess.**

   This answer is not correct because there is nothing in the story to indicate that Shobei felt the need or desire for more wealth.

4. **Which detail from the folktale helped you make your prediction?**

   Ⓐ **In return, the boy's mother gave Shobei three juicy oranges for his journey.**

   This answer is not correct because it does not tell about the villagers. It tells about someone else's act in response to Shobei's generosity.

   Ⓑ **As Shobei continued on his way, a dragonfly buzzed annoyingly around his head, so he caught it and tied the straw around its tail.**

   This answer is not correct because it does not indicate anything about Shobei's actions toward the villagers.

   ● **Shobei used his money wisely by purchasing many fields, which he divided equally among the people of his village.**

   This answer is correct because it tells about Shobei's generosity toward the villagers. You can predict that this behavior will lead to a feeling of respect toward Shobei.

   Ⓓ **When the princess asked Shobei for the fine cloth, he gladly gave it to her.**

   This answer is not correct because it tells about Shobei's generosity toward the princess, not the villagers.

MORE TO KNOW	• In fiction, predictions can be about future events or a character's thoughts, feelings, words, and actions. • In nonfiction, predictions can be about future events, people, places, and ideas.

Read this story about what happens to Cass during a power failure. Then answer the questions.

After finishing supper and loading the dishwasher, Cass retreated to her room to do homework. BANG! While logging in to check her assignments, Cass's computer screen went black.

"What was *that*?" cried Cass as she fumbled for a flashlight. While Dad checked the home's electric panel for tripped circuit breakers, Cass stepped on the porch and spotted an oak tree that had crashed into the O'Leary's front yard.

"I know what caused the neighborhood blackout," Cass declared.

After word processing her English essay, Cass had planned to shop online for her parents' anniversary gift and e-mail her friends to chat, but without electricity her personal computer wouldn't function. Illuminated by moonlight, she paced the house like a caged lion.

"How did people manage in the old days? My cell phone isn't charged, and my laptop hasn't been repaired yet," whined Cass.

"Your mother and I survived without high-tech electronics," laughed Dad.

Nodding, Cass realized that she could also survive without modern technology, and she devised a solution. Using a corded phone, she dialed a classmate and inquired about the essay topic. Then she rummaged around for a legal pad and pen and crowed, "Tonight won't be a total loss. And this assignment will not be late," she added confidently.

5. Which prediction is probably the most accurate?
   Ⓐ Cass will use a cell phone to call up her friends to chat.
   Ⓑ Cass will use a corded phone to call up her friends to chat.
   Ⓒ Cass will use a neighbor's computer to e-mail her friends.
   Ⓓ Cass will write friendly letters to her friends.

6. Predict what would most likely have occurred if the oak tree had not fallen.
   Ⓐ Cass would have used her personal computer to write her English essay.
   Ⓑ Cass would have used her laptop to write her English essay.
   Ⓒ Cass would have gone to the movies with her friends.
   Ⓓ Cass would have gone to a store to buy her parents' gift.

7. Predict what would have occurred if Cass had lacked access to a working phone.
   Ⓐ Cass would have walked to her classmate's house to get the English assignment.
   Ⓑ Cass would have stayed home from school the next day.
   Ⓒ Cass would have turned in her English assignment late.
   Ⓓ Cass would have driven to the repair shop to get her laptop.

8. Which of these will Cass most likely do next?
   Ⓐ Cass will toss her cell phone.
   Ⓑ Cass will handwrite her English essay on a pad of legal-sized paper.
   Ⓒ Cass will decide not to get her parents an anniversary gift.
   Ⓓ Cass will go next door to visit the neighbors.

Read this weblog entry written by a girl named Anne. Then answer the questions.

Anne's Blog

Wednesday, July 8

It seems like I have been at Camp Massapoag forever. The camp is on a big lake, and it has a long name that I can't spell—or even pronounce very easily. The camp is run by the Salvation Army and is for inner-city kids. My mom didn't want me hanging around the apartment all summer. She thought it would be good for me to get away and be on my own for two weeks, but I've never been so homesick in my life!

On my first day, I thought about running away. I told one of the other girls, but she was a blabbermouth and told one of the counselors, Miss Picket. I wasn't really going to run away, but Miss Picket still lectured me about how irresponsible it would be. She then let me send an e-mail to my mom to tell her to come get me. I think it was a trick, but I still did what she said.

This morning the counselors lined us up in pairs because they wanted us to have a buddy for our first day of swimming lessons. My buddy was a girl name Kiko, who was really nice. Then we went canoeing. The life jacket almost strangled me, but it was still fun. The girls in my canoe were also homesick, so I didn't feel quite so alone. In fact, I feel less homesick as each day goes by. Even the plan for stories around a campfire doesn't sound so bad anymore.

After lunch, we went for a nature hike. On the trail our leader explained all about the trees and the plants we saw. After the hike, it was time for arts and crafts. I made a picture frame for my mother, which looks hideous. But my mom is supportive of such efforts on my part.

It's been four days since I wrote my mom and she hasn't come for me yet, so I guess she's going to make me stick it out for another week. Even if she did come, she wouldn't recognize me. There was one plant our guide forgot to identify on our nature hike—poison ivy! Now I have a disgusting itchy rash over most of my body, and I have to wear this white lotion that makes me look like a walking statue. Maybe my mom will feel guilty and at least give me a choice about coming here again next year. But I doubt it.

9. Which of these is something Anne will most likely do at camp?
   Ⓐ tell stories around a campfire
   Ⓑ run away
   Ⓒ attend math classes
   Ⓓ watch a movie at a local theater

10. Predict how Anne's mother will react when she sees the picture frame.
    Ⓐ She'll shriek that it is hideous.
    Ⓑ She'll ask what it is supposed to be.
    Ⓒ She'll exclaim how lovely it is.
    Ⓓ She'll put it away and never mention it.

11. Which prediction is probably the most accurate?
    Ⓐ Anne will begin to enjoy camp more and more each day.
    Ⓑ Anne will write her mother another e-mail.
    Ⓒ Anne will beg Miss Picket to let her go home.
    Ⓓ Anne will mope around the camp until it's time to go home.

12. What will Anne's mother probably do next summer?
    Ⓐ She'll tell Anne that she never has to go to camp again.
    Ⓑ She'll sign Anne up for another two-week session at the camp.
    Ⓒ She'll let Anne stay home and do nothing all summer.
    Ⓓ She'll tell Anne that she can spend the whole summer at camp.

TEST TIPS

- A test question about making a prediction may ask you to predict what will happen next in a reading passage or what might happen in the future.
- A test question about making a prediction usually contains the words *predict, probably,* or *most likely.*
- The answer to a test question about making a prediction is never stated directly in a reading passage. You must link clues from the passage with what you know from your own experiences to make a prediction.

Read this poem by Walt Whitman. Then answer questions about the poem. Choose the best answer for Numbers 13 and 14.

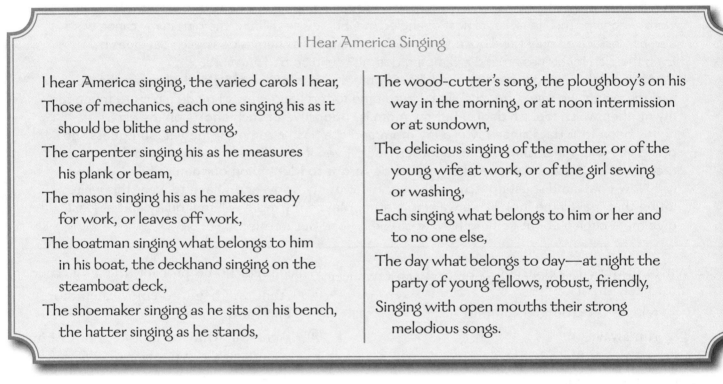

I Hear America Singing

I hear America singing, the varied carols I hear,
Those of mechanics, each one singing his as it
    should be blithe and strong,
The carpenter singing his as he measures
    his plank or beam,
The mason singing his as he makes ready
    for work, or leaves off work,
The boatman singing what belongs to him
    in his boat, the deckhand singing on the
    steamboat deck,
The shoemaker singing as he sits on his bench,
    the hatter singing as he stands,

The wood-cutter's song, the ploughboy's on his
    way in the morning, or at noon intermission
    or at sundown,
The delicious singing of the mother, or of the
    young wife at work, or of the girl sewing
    or washing,
Each singing what belongs to him or her and
    to no one else,
The day what belongs to day—at night the
    party of young fellows, robust, friendly,
Singing with open mouths their strong
    melodious songs.

13. Predict which of these statements the speaker of the poem would disagree with.
    Ⓐ America is a rich country, full of people with diverse occupations.
    Ⓑ Each person has something unique to contribute to America.
    Ⓒ People who know a trade are more interesting than people who do not know a trade.
    Ⓓ Each person contributes what he or she knows best.

14. Predict which of these attitudes the speaker of the poem would most likely have toward people who perform a service for others.
    Ⓐ narrow-mindedness
    Ⓑ compassion
    Ⓒ indifference
    Ⓓ disgust

Read this article about a unique hotel. Then answer questions about the article. Choose the best answer for Numbers 15 and 16.

Imagine visiting a hotel made entirely of ice. Not only is the hotel made of ice, so is its tables, chairs, and even its beds! If you're brave enough, you can stay at this hotel located on the shores of the Torne River in Sweden. The hotel is located about 120 miles north of the Arctic Circle. The temperature outside is chilly. Inside the hotel isn't much better—the inside temperature is about 23 degrees Fahrenheit.

The hotel has to be built from scratch every year because each spring the hotel melts. Every fall, workers begin building the structure. Construction begins in October. Workers use cannons to blast 30,000 tons of snow sprayed onto specially made metal molds to make the different sections of the structure. Once the snow is hard, the molds are removed and more molds are made. After construction is complete, the hotel boasts about 60 rooms, an ice chapel, an ice art exhibition hall, and an ice theater.

So what's it like to stay in the Ice Hotel? Guests sleep in special thermal sleeping bags on a bed made of snow and ice. Some rooms even have a skylight from which you can view the Aurora Borealis. These rooms also have a television, a phone, and a private bathroom. Other rooms have outdoor bathrooms accessible from the inside. Brrr!

In the morning, you will be greeted with a cup of hot drink made of mountain berries, along with an invitation to dine at the breakfast buffet. Then you can choose to visit the sauna.

Still think you've got what it takes to brave the cold? You're not alone. Each year, about 15,000 adventurers flock to the Ice Hotel to experience a world made entirely of snow and ice.

---

15. Who would most likely want to visit the Ice Hotel?
   - Ⓐ A person who enjoys spring and summer sports.
   - Ⓑ One who enjoys spending quiet time indoors by a warm fire.
   - Ⓒ Someone who enjoys a new adventure of any kind.
   - Ⓓ People who enjoy visiting museums and art exhibits.

16. Predict what will happen next April or May.
   - Ⓐ The Ice Hotel will begin to melt.
   - Ⓑ Thousands of visitors will stay in the hotel.
   - Ⓒ Construction will begin on the Ice Hotel.
   - Ⓓ Snow will be sprayed into snow molds.

Read this biography about Henry Bates, a scientist who spent many years studying insects. Then answer questions about the biography. Choose the best answer for Numbers 1 through 6.

Henry Bates, Explorer and Scientist

Henry Bates was born in England about 175 years ago. As a young man, he worked long hours in a sock-making factory. But his vocation was collecting insects and studying them. At the age of 22, Bates traveled to the Amazon rainforests of South America to study the fascinating creatures that lived there.

For 11 years, Bates explored the Amazon rain forests, collecting plants and insects. Living in the rain forest was extremely difficult. Bates was often ill and terribly lonely. Sometimes, he had no money for supplies. But he continued his studies because he was discovering insects that amazed and thrilled him. When Bates finally returned to England, he had collected about 15 thousand species of animals, mostly insects. More than 8 thousand of these species had never been seen by European scientists before.

Bates had many questions about the insects he had found. Why were there so many different ones? How was it possible for insects to look exactly like the rain-forest vegetation they were resting on? Similar to some known insects, these camouflaged insects were hiding from predators. But Bates wanted an explanation of how and why insects' bodies varied so much.

There were also insects that did not hide at all. They seemed to announce their presence with bold colors. Bates was particularly interested in the brightly colored butterflies. Many of them had flown slowly, too, making it easy for him to catch them. Why did they seem to draw attention to themselves? Why hadn't predators such as birds gobbled them all up?

In 1861, Bates presented a scientific paper about his discoveries. He explained that certain butterflies with bold colors and slow flights were poisonous. Predators were supposed to see them and avoid them. Butterflies with poisonous bodies and warning colors survived better than butterflies without warning colors. Those that survived produced offspring that looked and acted like them. Eventually, all the butterflies of a particular species had the same appearance and behaviors.

Recognizing Cause and Effect

1. Some butterflies have bright colors and fly slowly in order to
   (A) attract predators.
   (B) camouflage themselves.
   (C) discourage predators.
   (D) deceive scientists.

Comparing and Contrasting

4. In what way were the camouflaged insects and the brightly colored insects alike?
   (A) Both were eaten quickly.
   (B) Both were endangered species.
   (C) Both used color as a defense.
   (D) Both rested on vegetation.

Recognizing Cause and Effect

2. The graphic organizer shows a cause-and-effect relationship.

Cause	Effect
	Bates continued his studies even though life in the rain forest was so difficult.

   What belongs in the empty box?
   (A) Bates did not want to return to England.
   (B) Bates was discovering insects that amazed him.
   (C) Bates feared he would have to return to work in the sock-making factory.
   (D) Bates had no money for a return trip to England.

Making Predictions

5. Predict Bates's next step upon his return to England.
   (A) He will abandon his study of insects.
   (B) He will lecture at a university about his experience.
   (C) He will organize the data he collected in the rain forest.
   (D) He will write a story about his childhood.

Comparing and Contrasting

3. Which clue word signals how the insects of the rain forest are like other, known insects?
   (A) however
   (B) similar
   (C) same
   (D) alike

Making Predictions

6. Where or how did you find clues to help you make your prediction?
   (A) in the title of the story
   (B) in the pictures included with the story
   (C) in the details about the number of insect species Bates collected
   (D) by thinking about whether I like insects or not

Read this selection from a mystery novel. Then answer questions about the selection. Choose the best answer for Numbers 7 through 12.

When I awoke that morning and gazed upon my gloomy surroundings, I felt the cold fingers of dread pass over my body. How had I arrived in this unfamiliar chamber? I couldn't remember the events of last night. My head throbbed; my limbs ached; I groaned. Where was I exactly? I didn't recognize the four-poster bed with its heavy velvet curtains that enclosed me. When I peeked between the curtains, all was dark except for a crack of light gleaming beneath the chamber door.

Then I heard a gentle yet persistent rapping upon it. My troubled heart skipped a few beats, but I quickly caught my breath and called, "Who's there?"

"Your host," a deep, even voice responded to my inquiry.

"My host? But who are you?" I asked again, rising from my bed.

"Please permit me to enter and I will explain as best I can," my host replied sincerely. Gathering my composure, I opened the door.

The sight before me was quite extraordinary. My host was exquisitely dressed in black coat-and-tails, but his face was as white as alabaster, perhaps accented by his long, gray hair. His fire-red eyes were fixed on me.

"I found you slumped over the steering wheel of your car alongside the highway," he explained. "You must have fallen asleep and swerved off the road. You're fortunate to be alive. The front end of your car caved in completely when you hit the oak tree."

"I can't believe this has happened . . . it's no wonder I feel so terrible," I replied. "So sorry to be rude. I'm James Fielding. Thank you for your kind assistance, Mr. . . .?"

"Talbot, Henry Talbot. You may, of course, remain here at my estate as long as you require," he added.

"I think I have a concussion," I said, cradling my forehead in my hand. "I must see a physician. Is there someone nearby who would make a house call?"

"I don't think that will be necessary. My private nurse has already examined you thoroughly. Please rest until this evening, and then if you are faring no better, my chauffeur will convey you to the hospital."

"I must insist that he take me now, Mr. Talbot," I gripped the doorframe as a wave of dizziness came over me. Stars glimmered in my vision until, suddenly, their light dimmed. As I began to sink, my host grasped me by the arm.

"Fielding, you are in no condition to go anywhere," he insisted.

I tried to insist again, but my voice failed me along with my limbs. My host dragged me back into the dark chamber and hoisted me into that magnificent bed. The last thing I recall before slipping into unconsciousness was his strange face and the awful smirk upon it.

Recognizing Cause and Effect

7. According to Talbot, how did Fielding arrive at his estate?

    (A) After accidentally hitting Fielding in the head, Talbot drove him there.

    (B) After accepting Talbot's invitation, Fielding drove there.

    (C) After falling ill, Fielding collapsed on Talbot's doorstep.

    (D) After rescuing Fielding from an accident, Talbot brought him there.

Comparing and Contrasting

10. What was most noticeable about Talbot's clothing as compared to his physical appearance?

    (A) He wore the clothes of a gentleman, but he looked like a ghoul.

    (B) He sounded human when he spoke, but his appearance was that of a beast.

    (C) He wore a wrinkled old suit, but he looked healthy.

    (D) His words seemed insincere, but his appearance was honest.

Recognizing Cause and Effect

8. Talbot saw no need to take Fielding to a hospital because

    (A) Fielding's car was inoperable.

    (B) Fielding appeared to be overreacting.

    (C) Talbot's chauffeur was not available.

    (D) Talbot's nurse had already examined him.

Making Predictions

11. What will most likely happen next in the story?

    (A) Fielding will never regain consciousness.

    (B) Talbot will try to prevent Fielding from leaving again.

    (C) Fielding will awaken and drive away in his car.

    (D) Talbot will take Fielding to the hospital right away.

Comparing and Contrasting

9. Fielding compares Talbot's face to

    (A) stars.

    (B) velvet.

    (C) alabaster.

    (D) putty.

Making Predictions

12. Predict what the nature of Talbot's intentions for Fielding will prove to be.

    (A) disorganized

    (B) nurturing

    (C) treacherous

    (D) beneficial

FINDING WORD MEANING IN CONTEXT

PART ONE: Think About the Strategy

What Is Word Meaning in Context?

Sometimes when you speak with someone, you hear a word that you've never heard before. Many times you can figure out the meaning of the word by thinking about how the person uses it.

1 Write what you think the word *intact* means. It's okay if you don't know the real meaning. Just make a good guess.

_____

_____

2 Someone says to you: "<u>Many items were damaged when I dropped the box, but the vase remained intact</u>." Write what you think the word *intact* means now.

_____

_____

3 Write the clues in the underlined sentence that helped you figure out what the word *intact* means.

_____

_____

Work with a Partner

- Make a list of five challenging words that you know the meaning of. Ask your partner which words he or she doesn't know.
- Use each of the words your partner doesn't know in a sentence or two that give good hints about the word's meaning. See if your partner can figure out what the word means.
- Then have your partner do the same for you.

How Do You Find Word Meaning in Context?

You can find word meaning in context when you come to a new word in a reading passage. Look for clues to help you figure out what the word means. Clues might be in the sentence where the word is found. Clues may also be in the sentence just before or just after the one where the word is found.

Read this passage about deer. See if you can figure out what the word *forage* means.

> As more housing developments are built, there are fewer and fewer places for wildlife. In particular, deer are finding themselves crowded out of their natural habitat. They often wander into neighborhoods and forage for food in people's backyards. Residents complain that deer find their gardens, and the vegetables are being eaten up and destroyed. But there is little that can be done. As long as deer lose more and more of their habitat, the problem will likely get worse before it gets better.

1. Let's narrow down the clues to figure out what the word *forage* means.

   Look at the chart below.
   It shows three sentences: the one that comes before the word *forage*, the one that contains the word *forage*, and the one that comes after the word *forage*.

   Look carefully at the sentences that come before and after the word *forage*.

In particular, deer are finding themselves crowded out of their natural habitat.	They often wander into neighborhoods and forage for food in people's backyards.	Residents complain that deer find their gardens, and the vegetables are being eaten up and destroyed.
Before		After

2. Now think about what the clues in the sentences tell you:

   Deer are losing their habitat. This is where they live and find food. They wander into neighborhoods where residents complain that their vegetable gardens are being eaten up and destroyed. What are the deer doing in the neighborhoods? They are probably searching for food that they can't find in their natural habitat.

3. So, the word *forage* must mean _____

   _____ .

WHAT TO KNOW	When you figure out the meaning of an unknown word from other words, you are **finding word meaning in context**. The words and phrases around an unknown word often provide clues to the word's meaning. These clues are called **context clues**. • Context clues are often in the sentence where the unknown word appears. They can also be in the sentences before and after the word. • Synonyms of the unknown word are often context clues. • Antonyms of the unknown word are often context clues. • A comparison or a definition often provides clues to the meaning of an unknown word.

Read this story about a girl with a huge appetite. As you read, think about the meaning of the word *gulps* in the second sentence and the other words that point to its meaning.

Mealtime for Rhylla

At the pizzeria one evening, Rhylla finished off a slice of pizza in a few huge bites. Then in a few hefty gulps she finished her favorite soda. "What's for dessert tonight?" she inquired of the waiter.

With a wide smile, he replied, "How about a pie?"

Rhylla just laughed and said, "Maybe I better have a spinach salad instead."

You can figure out the meaning of the word *gulps* by looking at the words and phrases around it. The words *hefty* and *finished* are clues to the meaning of the word *gulps*. The phrase *a few huge bites* is also a clue. This phrase describes how Rhylla ate her pizza, which gives a clue about how she probably finished her soda.

The meaning of the word *gulps* is "large amounts swallowed at one time."

Read this Norse myth about Odin. As you read, ask yourself, "Which context clues will help me figure out the meaning of the word *runes*?" Then answer the questions.

Odin

In Norse mythology, Odin is best known as the most important of the warrior gods who resided behind the walls of Asgard. However, Odin is also the god of poetry and wisdom. He attained this status through great personal sacrifice. In one instance, he hanged himself on the world tree, a giant ash called Yggdrasil. Pierced by his own spear, he survived there for nine days in a trance. During this trial, he learned nine powerful songs and eighteen runes. These symbols brought written language to the Norse people.

1. The word *runes* probably means
   - Ⓐ "poetry."
   - Ⓑ "wisdom."
   - Ⓒ "symbols."
   - Ⓓ "recipes."

2. Which kind of clue hints at the meaning of the word *runes*?
   - Ⓐ a synonym
   - Ⓑ an antonym
   - Ⓒ a definition
   - Ⓓ a comparison

Work with a Partner

- Talk about your answers to the questions.
- Tell why you chose your answers.
- Then talk about what you have learned so far about finding word meaning in context.

REVIEW

Context clues help you figure out the meaning of an unfamiliar word.

- Look for context clues in the sentence where the unknown word appears. Look also in the sentences before and after the word.
- Look for synonyms that may help you figure out the meaning of an unknown word.
- Look for antonyms that may help you figure out the meaning of an unknown word.
- Look for a comparison or a definition that may help you figure out the meaning of an unknown word.

Read this report about homes in ancient Roman towns. As you read, think about how you will figure out the meaning of any words that are unfamiliar to you. Then answer the questions.

domus

insulae

Roman Homes

Like modern cities of today, ancient Roman towns were busy places. These towns were congested with the many people who lived and worked there. In Roman towns, homes were built directly along the streets. These homes had no frontage, with the possible exception of a sidewalk, separating them from the chaotic streets.

The majority of the people lived in *insulae*, which resembled an apartment complex. Insulae consisted of several apartment buildings constructed around a small, central courtyard. An *insula* had between three and five stories. On the first story of the apartment building were shops. The stories above contained small apartments of a few multi-purpose rooms. Any room with a window faced the busy street.

Only the wealthiest people could afford to live in a private home called a *domus*. A domus had a main living area of several rooms built around an inner courtyard, called an *atrium*. The rooms opened onto the atrium, which brought necessary light and air into the home. Beyond the main living area, there might be a larger courtyard called a *peristyle*. Rooms with windows faced the atrium or peristyle rather than the street.

3. In the last paragraph, what is the meaning of the word *domus*?

Ⓐ "an apartment complex"

Ⓑ "a private home"

Ⓒ "a shop"

Ⓓ "a room"

4. Which of these gives a clue to the meaning of the word *domus*?

Ⓐ a synonym

Ⓑ an antonym

Ⓒ a definition

Ⓓ a comparison

Which Answer Is Correct and Why?

Look at the answer choices for each question.
Read why each answer choice is correct or not correct.

3. In the last paragraph, what is the meaning of the word *domus*?

   Ⓐ "an apartment complex"

   This answer is not correct because in paragraph 2, the article defines a Roman apartment complex as *insulae*.

   ⬤ "a private home"

   This answer is correct because in the last paragraph, a *domus* is described as a private home.

   Ⓒ "a shop"

   This answer is not correct because a *domus* was a private home, not a shop.

   Ⓓ "a room"

   This answer is not correct because the context clues in the article describe a *domus* as having rooms. Therefore, a *domus* could not be a single room.

4. Which of these gives a clue to the meaning of the word *domus*?

   Ⓐ a synonym

   This answer is not correct because there is no synonym for the word *domus* in the article.

   Ⓑ an antonym

   This answer is not correct because there is no antonym for *domus* in the article.

   ⬤ a definition

   This answer is correct because the article states that: *"Only the wealthiest people could afford to live in a private home called a domus."* This sentence gives the meaning of the word *domus*.

   Ⓓ a comparison

   This answer is not correct because there is no comparison in the article that gives the meaning of the word *domus*.

MORE
TO
KNOW

- Context clues are especially helpful when trying to figure out the meaning of scientific or technical terms and foreign-language words.
- Substituting another word for the unfamiliar word is a good way to check your understanding.
- The tone and the setting of a reading passage can sometimes help you figure out the meaning of an unfamiliar word.

Read this science article about the human heart. Then answer the questions.

The Heart

Inside the chest is a strong muscle called the heart, which is often compared to a pump. The heart circulates blood throughout the body. This circulation of blood is absolutely vital. Through vessels, blood carries oxygen and nutrients to every organ and cell of the body, and carries waste away. Without oxygen, the brain cannot survive for more than ten minutes.

The heart has two sides. On the left side, blood flows into the heart, carrying oxygen from the lungs. The heart pumps the oxygen-rich blood through the arteries and smaller capillaries to the body, and the body uses the oxygen in the blood. On the right side, blood flows from the body (via the veins) into the heart. The heart pumps the oxygen-poor blood to the lungs. Both sides of the heart work together simultaneously.

The heart pumps involuntarily at a steady pace. The actual number of heartbeats per minute, or pulse, is one way the health of the heart can be assessed. Doctors use this figure as a basic measurement of the heart's strength.

5. You can tell that *vital* in the first paragraph means
   Ⓐ "unnecessary for life."
   Ⓑ "essential to life."
   Ⓒ "lifeless."
   Ⓓ "lively."

6. What is the best meaning of the word *pulse*?
   Ⓐ "a steady heartbeat"
   Ⓑ "a measurement of the heart's size"
   Ⓒ "a rapid pace"
   Ⓓ "the number of heartbeats per minute"

7. *Arteries, capillaries,* and *veins* can best be described as
   Ⓐ blood vessels.
   Ⓑ little pumps.
   Ⓒ blood cells.
   Ⓓ unnecessary organs.

8. In the last paragraph, which phrase gives a clue to the meaning of *assessed*?
   Ⓐ "pumps involuntarily"
   Ⓑ "actual number of beats"
   Ⓒ "at a steady pace"
   Ⓓ "measurement of the heart's strength"

Read this history article about an African American cultural movement. Then answer the questions.

The Harlem Renaissance

In the 1920s, a cultural movement developed, centered in New York City's Harlem community. Here, the literature, art, and music of African Americans experienced a rebirth. It was known as the Harlem Renaissance. The movement was based on creative talent and a growth of racial pride among African Americans. In their works, these authors, artists, and musicians celebrated the black culture of the North and South. They also celebrated their African heritage.

Many arts flourished during the Harlem Renaissance. Of them, literature is the best known today. Probably the most famous is the work of the poet Langston Hughes. Hughes created his poems with the rhythms of jazz and the rich language of everyday dialect. Other well-known authors include the novelists Zora Neale Hurston, Jean Toomer, and Claude McKay.

Langston Hughes

9. In the article, *renaissance* means
   Ⓐ "a reaction."
   Ⓑ "a reflection."
   Ⓒ "a rebirth."
   Ⓓ "a reversal."

10. In the first paragraph, *the North and South* refers to
   Ⓐ two different countries.
   Ⓑ two major regions of the United States.
   Ⓒ two states in Mexico.
   Ⓓ two provinces of Canada.

11. In the last paragraph, you can tell that *dialect* means
   Ⓐ "a form of speech."
   Ⓑ "a familiar song."
   Ⓒ "a secret code."
   Ⓓ "the written word."

12. The word *flourished* is in the last paragraph. You can tell that *flourished* means
   Ⓐ "lived well."
   Ⓑ "grew or developed vigorously."
   Ⓒ "made a lot of noise."
   Ⓓ "gradually died out."

TEST TIPS

- A test question about finding meaning in context asks you about the meaning of a word from a reading passage. The word may or may not be familiar to you. The word might also be used in a new way.

- A test question about finding meaning in context usually has several answer choices. If you have difficulty answering the question, try each answer choice in the sentence in which the word appears. Decide which answer choice makes the most sense in the reading passage.

Read this travel article about Montreal. Then answer questions about the article. Choose the best answer for Numbers 13 and 14.

Travel to Montreal

Located in the heart of French Quebec, Montreal is an international city. It has a thriving culture, full of *joie de vivre*. Travelers can take in the performing arts, art festivals, historical sites, and museums. On the lively streets of Montreal, one might hear as many as 35 languages. Many of the languages are spoken by immigrants who have recently made Montreal their home. Not surprisingly, restaurants provide flavorful fare from around the world. And the shopping! A traveler can find just about anything desired, from the exotic to the everyday!

13. In the article, *joie de vivre* means
Ⓐ "joyful living."
Ⓑ "limited activities."
Ⓒ "sadness of life."
Ⓓ "wealthy people."

14. The words *flavorful fare* refer to
Ⓐ reasonable rates.
Ⓑ pleasant music.
Ⓒ tasty food.
Ⓓ lavish gifts.

Read this article about bears. Then answer questions about the article. Choose the best answer for Numbers 15 and 16.

Most people believe that bears hibernate. However, according to the scientific definition, what bears actually do resembles more of a deep sleep than hibernation. The reason for hibernation and for deep winter sleep is the same. During the winter months, food is scarce. It is also difficult for some animals to maintain their normal body temperature. As a result, many animals hibernate and live off their stored body fat.

When an animal hibernates, its metabolism and body temperature are reduced significantly. This keeps any growth or development at a minimum. A bear goes into a deep sleep during the cold days of winter, but it does not reduce its growth as much as a true hibernator. Animals use less energy when they sleep than when they are active. Bears save energy by sleeping. Because they are not true hibernators, they can wake up during the winter and move to another location if needed.

As winter approaches, bears fatten up with several months of good eating. Then they search for a cozy den to snooze through the cold winter months and live off their stored fat. When spring arrives, bears wake up very hungry!

Scientists in Yellowstone Park found out that grizzly bears are likely to choose dens where they won't be disturbed. Some of the dens are right on canyon walls where it is difficult for any person or animal to intrude. Grizzly bears line the dens with a fine insulation of pine and fir branches.

It has also recently been uncovered that grizzly bears will not enter their dens for their winter sleep until the start of a blizzard. They act on a natural instinct of self-preservation. The blizzard quickly covers the bears' tracks as they enter the dens. The snow serves as a protection for them. No one would know that a sleeping bear is curled up deep inside the den.

15. In the article, *minimum* means
    Ⓐ "what is normal or typical."
    Ⓑ "the largest or greatest amount."
    Ⓒ "unusual or unexpected"
    Ⓓ "the lowest possible amount."

16. A grizzly bear's instinct for *self-preservation* helps the bear to
    Ⓐ sleep during the coldest months.
    Ⓑ remain hidden without being found.
    Ⓒ continue growing while it sleeps.
    Ⓓ slow down its breathing.

Lesson 8
DRAWING CONCLUSIONS AND MAKING INFERENCES

PART ONE: Think About the Strategy

What Are Conclusions and Inferences?

There are many times each day when you figure out something on your own without being told what is happening. If you see a dog sitting inside by a door, you can figure out that the dog probably wants to go outside. If you see someone wearing shorts and a T-shirt, you know that the weather is probably warm.

1 Write something that you figured out on your own about someone in your family.

_____

_____

_____

_____

2 Write the clues that helped you figure this out.

_____

_____

_____

_____

Work with a Partner

- Take turns asking each other "What is going on?" questions.
- Ask questions such as "If someone has pajamas on and has just yawned and set an alarm clock, what is the person probably doing?"

How Do You Draw Conclusions and Make Inferences?

There are many times when you read that you draw conclusions or make inferences. Sometimes the author does not give you all the details. You need to figure something out by yourself. An author might describe a place where kangaroos and wallabies roam free. The author does not tell you that the story takes place in Australia. But you can use passage clues and what you already know to figure this out on your own.

Read this passage about last names. See what you can figure out on your own.

> Many last names reflect the occupations once held by family members with that name. Two such common names are Baker and Carpenter. Two less obvious names related to occupations are Collier and Coward. Collier is a medieval word meaning "coal man," and the name Coward comes from the term *cow-herd*, meaning "one who herds cows."

1. Let's draw a conclusion.

   Think about what the author tells you.
   Also think about what is just suggested.

2. Look at the chart below.

   The first box tells details that are directly given in the passage.
   The second box tells what is suggested but not directly stated.

3. Think about the details that are given, along with your own background knowledge.

4. Fill in the missing information in the last box to tell what you can figure out.

What details are given?	What information is not directly stated?	What can you figure out on your own?
Some last names reflect the occupations once held by family members of that name.	The author does not state what kind of work people with the name Baker or Carpenter did. The author does not state what kind of work was done by people with the name Collier or Coward.	People with the last name Baker or Carpenter had a family member who was once a baker or a carpenter. People who were named _____ were coal miners. People with the last name Coward had family members who were once _____ _____ .

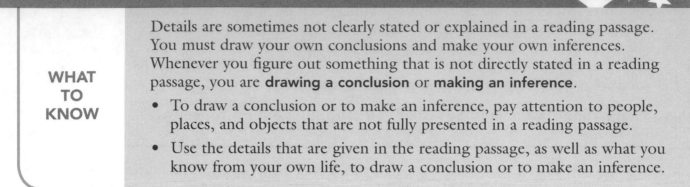

WHAT TO KNOW

Details are sometimes not clearly stated or explained in a reading passage. You must draw your own conclusions and make your own inferences. Whenever you figure out something that is not directly stated in a reading passage, you are **drawing a conclusion** or **making an inference**.

- To draw a conclusion or to make an inference, pay attention to people, places, and objects that are not fully presented in a reading passage.

- Use the details that are given in the reading passage, as well as what you know from your own life, to draw a conclusion or to make an inference.

Read this paragraph from an article about a form of dance and music called salsa. As you read, see if you can figure out which forms of music have influenced salsa.

Salsa is a form of Latin dance and music. It had its origins in Cuba, Puerto Rico, or New York City. It depends on who you ask. In the United States, salsa is a combination of Afro-Caribbean music and rhythms. It also has elements of jazz, rock, and swing. Salsa is becoming more and more popular. According to one Latino author, Mambo, Cha-Cha-Cha, and Merengue are three popular dances in California. Guaguanco and Guajira are still danced in New York, Puerto Rico, and Florida.

This paragraph does not tell you which forms of music have influenced salsa. It does, however, provide the following details, which you can use as clues to figure out this information on your own.

In the United States, salsa is a combination of Afro-Caribbean music and rhythms. It also has elements of jazz, rock, and swing.

These detail clues help you determine that jazz, rock, and swing have influenced salsa. From your own experience, you may already know that these are also types of music.

Read this excerpt from a fairy tale about a water nymph named Clytie. As you read, look for details that will help you figure out the reason for Clytie's behavior. Then answer the questions.

Long ago, a water nymph named Clytie lived in a cave at the bottom of the sea, surrounded by a lush forest of coral and sea fans. Behind the cave were Clytie's gardens. Here she spent long hours tending to her sea anemones and her star lilies. She kept her favorite horses, the swift-darting goldfish and the slow-moving turtles, in the garden grotto.

For a long time, she was very happy and contented. But one day, she heard the mermaid's song that told of a glorious light, which shone on top of the water. After Clytie heard this song, she thought of nothing else and longed to see the wonderful light. But no sea nymph dared take her to it, and she grew very unhappy. Soon, she neglected her garden and all her sea creatures.

In vain, the other nymphs begged her to forget the enchanting light. They told her that no sea nymph had ever seen it, or ever could hope to see it. But Clytie would not listen, and she spent more and more of her time in her shell carriage, riding far away from her cave. In this way, she could dream, undisturbed, of the glorious light.

1. You can tell that Clytie spent more time away from her cave because she

Ⓐ   thought she might be able to find the way to the light on her own.

Ⓑ   wanted to make the other sea nymphs angry.

Ⓒ   believed it would be the only way to stop dreaming about the light.

Ⓓ   hoped to avoid the sight of her untended garden.

2. Which clue in the fairy tale helped you figure out why Clytie spent more time away from her cave?

Ⓐ   Soon, she neglected her garden . . .

Ⓑ   . . . longed to see the wonderful light.

Ⓒ   . . . she could dream, undisturbed, of the glorious light.

Ⓓ   In vain, the other nymphs . . .

Work with a Partner

• Talk about your answers to the questions.

• Tell why you chose your answers.

• Then talk about what you have learned so far about drawing conclusions and making inferences.

Drawing a conclusion or making an inference is a way of figuring out information that is suggested but not directly stated in a reading passage.

- Think about the details that are provided in a reading passage. Use these details to figure out or understand information that is not fully explained.

- Use the facts you have learned from your reading and what you know from your own life to draw a conclusion or to make an inference.

Read the next part of the story about Clytie. As you read, ask yourself, "What details in the fairy tale help me figure out what is happening? What do I know from my own life that will help me figure out what is happening?" Then answer the questions.

Now it happened late one summer night, when the sea was warm and the turtles were moving very slowly, Clytie fell asleep. Unguided, the turtles swam on and on, up and up, through the green waters, until they reached the surface, close to a wooded island.

As the waves dashed the carriage against the shore, Clytie awoke. Trembling and filled with wonder, she climbed out of the shell and sat upon a rock. The waking world was very beautiful. The forest wind rustled through the leaves. The fragrance of flowers and grass rose from the meadows.

She was dazed by all these wonders and she thought she must be dreaming, but soon she forgot all about them, for the eastern sky blazed suddenly with light. Great purple curtains were lifted, and slowly there appeared a great ball of dazzling fire, which blinded her eyes with its beauty. She held her breath and stretched out her arms toward it, for she knew at once that this was the glorious light she had dreamed about and longed for.

In the midst of the light was a golden chariot, drawn by four fiery steeds, and in the chariot sat a smiling king, with seven rays of light playing around his crown. As the steeds mounted higher and higher in their path, birds began to sing, plants opened their buds, and even the old sea looked happy.

3. What can readers conclude about the light that Clytie found?
   - Ⓐ It was the moon rising in the evening.
   - Ⓑ It was one of the seven rays from the king's crown.
   - Ⓒ It was the sun rising in the morning.
   - Ⓓ It was the sun setting in the evening.

4. You can tell that Clytie
   - Ⓐ told the turtles to take her to the surface of the water.
   - Ⓑ had no idea where the turtles had taken her.
   - Ⓒ will return immediately to her real home.
   - Ⓓ would not have reached the surface of the water had she not fallen asleep.

Which Answer Is Correct and Why?

**Look at the answer choices for each question.
Read why each answer choice is correct or not correct.**

3. **What can readers conclude about the light that Clytie found?**

   Ⓐ **It was the moon rising in the evening.**

   This answer is not correct because the details in the fairy tale tell about *"great purple curtains"* lifting and the eastern sky blazing with light. These details suggest that the sun is rising, not the moon. If the moon was rising, the sky would not blaze with light.

   Ⓑ **It was one of the seven rays from the king's crown.**

   This answer is not correct because Clytie had already seen the light before the king appeared.

   ● **It was the sun rising in the morning.**

   This answer is correct because at least two details support it. Paragraph 2 states that the *"waking world was very beautiful."* The word *waking* indicates that it is close to dawn. Paragraph 3 states that the *"eastern sky blazed suddenly with light."* You probably already know from your own experience that the sun rises in the east and sets in the west.

   Ⓓ **It was the sun setting in the evening.**

   This answer is not correct because the details tell that the eastern sky blazed with light. These details suggest that the sun is rising, not setting.

4. **You can tell that Clytie**

   Ⓐ **told the turtles to take her to the surface of the water.**

   This answer is not correct because the details in the fairy tale explain that the turtles were unguided as they swam.

   Ⓑ **had no idea where the turtles had taken her.**

   This answer is not correct because the details explain that Clytie knew that the light she saw was the light she had dreamed about and longed for.

   Ⓒ **will return immediately to her real home.**

   This answer is not correct because there are no details that suggest Clytie will return home right away. Also, she had wanted so much to see the light, it's unlikely that she'd want to leave it right away once she'd found it.

   ● **would not have reached the surface of the water had she not fallen asleep.**

   This answer is correct because details explain that Clytie had fallen asleep and the turtles were unguided as they swam up and up. You know that Clytie did not know the way to the light herself. You can determine from detail clues that had Clytie not been asleep, she probably would not have directed the turtles to travel in the direction that they did.

Drawing Conclusions and Making Inferences 87

MORE TO KNOW	• Look for details in a reading passage that tell about how a person or character looks, acts, thinks, feels, and speaks. Think about how people with similar qualities behave. Also think about the times you may have behaved in a similar way yourself. • Think about the information you figured out on your own. Ask yourself, "Which details in the reading passage helped me draw this conclusion or make this inference?"

Read this article about the pyramids at Giza. Then answer the questions.

It had long been an accepted fact that the great pyramids at Giza were built by as many as 100,000 enslaved people. But recent evidence is casting doubt on these once-firm beliefs.

One international team of experts built a small model pyramid. They used the same basic technology available to the ancients. They quarried the stone blocks. They transported them to the site and then set the stones in place. Based on the number of workers it took to build the model, they figured out that as few as 5,000 workers could have built the core structure of the pyramid. This doesn't include the estimated 15,000 workers who performed the finish work. Still, the number is much lower than the estimate of 100,000 workers.

Egyptologists also studied hieroglyphic inscriptions inside the pyramids. These inscriptions describe the various kinds of workers, their titles, and how they were organized. The workers were artisans, inspectors, and directors. The workers were organized into crews. The crews had names like *Endurance, Perfection, Strength,* and *Friends of Khufu*. It seems that the crews competed with one another in the construction of sections of a pyramid. The winning crew inscribed their name in one of the stones. None of these findings points to slavery.

5. There is enough information in the article to conclude that
   - Ⓐ recent evidence indicates that 100,000 enslaved people built the pyramids.
   - Ⓑ recent evidence indicates about 20,000 workers willingly built the pyramids.
   - Ⓒ there is no good evidence about the number of workers available.
   - Ⓓ the new evidence about the number of workers is absolutely accurate.

6. From the article, you can figure out that
   - Ⓐ little has been learned about the pyramids.
   - Ⓑ there is little more that could be learned by studying the pyramids.
   - Ⓒ there is still disagreement about exactly how the pyramids were built.
   - Ⓓ there is no dispute about how the pyramids were built.

7. Readers of this article can conclude that
   - Ⓐ the ancients had advanced technology that is unavailable today.
   - Ⓑ women and children participated in the construction of the pyramid.
   - Ⓒ the model pyramid was smaller than the actual pyramid.
   - Ⓓ construction of the core structure took longer than the finish work.

8. The building of the pyramid was probably
   - Ⓐ flawed.
   - Ⓑ haphazard.
   - Ⓒ unorganized.
   - Ⓓ structured.

Read this article about folk songs known as spirituals. Then answer the questions.

Spirituals are folk songs created by African Americans during the time of slavery. Spirituals often spoke of the disappointments and injustices faced by slaves. They also spoke of the longing for freedom.

African Americans based many spirituals upon Christian hymns and stories. Many spirituals resemble prayers that ask for release from bondage. The songs also speak of African traditions. Many of the melodies and rhythms of the mournful songs originated in Africa.

Negro Spiritual
by Helene Sandeau

The exact number of spirituals is not known. Until after the Civil War, they were passed orally to each generation. Thomas Wentworth Higginson, a Union officer, was deeply moved by the spirituals sung by his African American soldiers. He first recorded several spirituals for the magazine *The Atlantic Monthly* in 1867. That same year, three Northerners published *Slave Songs of the United States*. This was the first systematic collection of songs.

Spirituals did not find popularity outside of the South until 1871. In that year, a group of students from Fisk University began giving concerts. They wanted to raise money for their school. From 1871 to 1875, the Jubilee Singers toured the world singing the songs that their parents had taught them. Spirituals received worldwide recognition during the twentieth century. Famous African American singers such as Paul Robeson, Marian Anderson, and Roland Hayes helped bring attention to these songs.

9. The article suggests that many spirituals are
   Ⓐ religious songs.
   Ⓑ joyful songs.
   Ⓒ war songs.
   Ⓓ children's songs.

10. Spirituals tell stories from the viewpoint of
    Ⓐ slave owners.
    Ⓑ Northerners.
    Ⓒ African Americans.
    Ⓓ Southerners.

11. Which of these would most likely have been the theme of some spirituals?
    Ⓐ carelessness
    Ⓑ despair
    Ⓒ affection
    Ⓓ enthusiasm

12. From the article, you can determine that
    Ⓐ interest in spirituals has declined in recent years.
    Ⓑ spirituals were not heard of until after the Civil War.
    Ⓒ the majority of spirituals were uplifting.
    Ⓓ most spirituals were not originally written down.

TEST TIPS

- A test question about drawing conclusions or making inferences asks you to figure out something that is not directly stated in a reading passage. Use information in the selection, combined with what you already know, to arrive at an answer.

- A test question about drawing conclusions or making inferences often contains the words *you can tell*, *determine*, or *conclude*.

Read this e-mail written by a young person with a dilemma. Then answer questions about the e-mail. Choose the best answer for Numbers 13 and 14.

To: EMJohnston247@fam.abc
From: PJJohnston32@tig.xyz
Subject: Tomorrow's visit

Grandma,

   I hope you will understand the problem I'm facing. I want to come to your house tomorrow for the visit we planned, but Tiger has disappeared. I would like to make sure I'm here in case he finds his way home. Last I saw him, Tiger was outside "hunting" the fall leaves that were dancing in the wind. I called for him all afternoon, but he didn't come bounding across the lawn as he usually does. I'm hoping he is just off chasing mice and wasn't scared up a tree by a dog. When that happened last year, it took three firefighters to get him down! Do you think it would be possible for you to visit at our house tomorrow instead? Let me know.
Love,
PJ

13. Readers of the e-mail can conclude that
    Ⓐ Tiger is PJ's pet cat.
    Ⓑ PJ does not really care to visit with grandma.
    Ⓒ Tiger has never been missing before.
    Ⓓ Grandmother will reschedule her visit with PJ.

14. From the e-mail, you can determine
    Ⓐ when Tiger will return.
    Ⓑ what time of year it is.
    Ⓒ how long Tiger has been gone.
    Ⓓ where Tiger is hiding.

90   Drawing Conclusions and Making Inferences

Read this article about eyeglasses. Then answer questions about the article. Choose the best answer for Numbers 15 and 16.

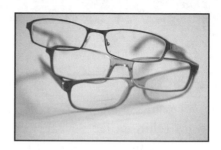

About half the population in the United States wear eyeglasses or contact lenses. Glasses and contact lenses correct a variety of vision difficulties. There have always been people with imperfect vision. However, there has not always been a way to correct it.

For centuries, people have known that certain shapes and materials magnified objects. In China, magnifying glasses made of glass or crystal were invented more than a thousand years ago. At about the same time, Arab scholars were studying the magnification properties of glass balls. Scientists who experimented with light and lenses learned that light enters the front of the eye and is focused on the back.

Methods for grinding glass and scientific information about the eye gradually spread to Europe. By the 1300s, Europeans were using glass magnifying lenses as aids to vision. It would take centuries, however, for inventors to design a practical way to keep the lenses on the head. Not until the late 1800s could people buy eyeglasses that had curved earpieces.

Magnifying lenses helped people who had difficulty seeing near things, such as print on a page. But what about those who couldn't see distant objects? This is called nearsightedness. Lens makers figured out how to correct this problem. Magnifying lenses curve outward. But lenses to correct nearsightedness curve inward. They are concave. To see something far away, a person would peer through a single concave lens attached to a ribbon. The device was known as a perspective glass.

By the 1700s, peddlers were selling all sorts of eyeglasses. People held up various glasses until they found the pair that generally improved their vision. People didn't go to a doctor to correct their vision until about one hundred years ago.

15. There is enough information in the article to conclude that
   Ⓐ it wasn't until the 1200s that people realized glass could magnify objects.
   Ⓑ not all vision problems can be corrected with lenses.
   Ⓒ magnifying lenses do not help people who are primarily nearsighted.
   Ⓓ All people have imperfect vision.

16. You can tell that
   Ⓐ people once corrected their vision without the help of a professional.
   Ⓑ only the wealthy were able to afford early eyeglasses.
   Ⓒ nearsightedness is the most common vision problem.
   Ⓓ a perspective glass was used mainly as a fashion accessory.

What Is a Fact?

Have you ever told someone the color of your eyes or the date on which your birthday falls? If so, you were telling a fact. A fact tells about something that can be proved. If you say, "I have over a hundred coins in my coin collection," you are telling a fact. You can prove it.

1 Write one fact about one of your favorite foods.

_____

_____

What Is an Opinion?

Have you ever told someone how you feel about something? If so, you were telling an opinion. An opinion tells what you think, feel, or believe. An opinion cannot be proved. If you say, "Fishing is boring," you are expressing an opinion. Probably not everyone thinks that fishing is boring.

2 Write one opinion about this same food.

_____

_____

3 Write how your fact is different from your opinion.

_____

_____

Work with a Partner

- Take turns telling a fact about something, such as a fact about a sport or a subject. Then express an opinion about the same thing.
- Talk about how your facts are different from your opinions.

How Do You Find Facts and Opinions?

Some reading passages have details that are facts, and some have details that are opinions. Many reading passages contain both facts and opinions. Here's how to tell the difference: If a detail can be checked or proved, it's a fact. If a detail tells what someone thinks, feels, or believes, it's an opinion.

Read this passage about South America. See if you can tell the facts from the opinions.

> South America is a great place to plan a vacation. People who enjoy sun and surf will love the beautiful beaches of Brazil. Serious hikers should check out the magnificent Andes Mountains. The mountain range runs all along the western edge of the continent. If you're very daring, you will want to explore the amazing Amazon River. The Amazon River is the second longest river in the world—about 4,000 miles long.

1. Let's think about which details in the passage are facts and which are opinions.

   Look at the chart below.

   A check mark in the second column indicates a fact. A check mark in the third column indicates an opinion.

2. Complete the chart by placing checkmarks in the appropriate boxes.

Detail	This detail can be checked or proved.	This detail tells what someone thinks, feels, or believes.
South America is a great place to plan a vacation.	☐ Fact	✓ Opinion
People who enjoy sun and surf will love beautiful beaches of Brazil.	☐ Fact	☐ Opinion
Serious hikers should check out the magnificent Andes Mountains.	☐ Fact	☐ Opinion
The mountain range runs all along the western edge of the continent.	✓ Fact	☐ Opinion
If you're very daring, you will want to explore the amazing Amazon River.	☐ Fact	✓ Opinion
The Amazon River is the second longest river in the world—about 4,000 miles long.	☐ Fact	☐ Opinion

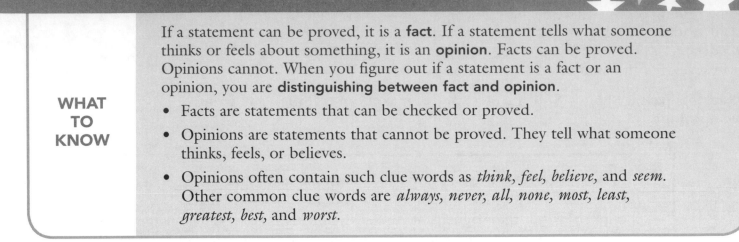

WHAT TO KNOW

If a statement can be proved, it is a **fact**. If a statement tells what someone thinks or feels about something, it is an **opinion**. Facts can be proved. Opinions cannot. When you figure out if a statement is a fact or an opinion, you are **distinguishing between fact and opinion**.

- Facts are statements that can be checked or proved.
- Opinions are statements that cannot be proved. They tell what someone thinks, feels, or believes.
- Opinions often contain such clue words as *think, feel, believe,* and *seem.* Other common clue words are *always, never, all, none, most, least, greatest, best,* and *worst.*

Read this article about a potato-chip study. As you read, look for statements that can be proved and for statements that tell what someone thinks, feels, or believes.

In one study, the average snack-size bag of regular potato chips had 12 grams of fat and 100 milligrams of salt. The fat content accounted for 18 percent of the daily recommended allowance. The salt content accounted for 25 percent. Reduced-fat potato chips had 7 grams of fat and 20 milligrams of salt. These potato chips accounted for 10 percent of the recommended fat allowance. They accounted for 5 percent of the recommended salt allowance. But regular potato chips taste better. You shouldn't waste your money on reduced-fat chips.

The statements that can be checked or proved are:

In one study, the average snack-size bag of regular potato chips had 12 grams of fat and 100 milligrams of salt.

The fat content accounted for 18 percent of the daily recommended allowance.

The salt content accounted for 25 percent.

Reduced-fat potato chips had 7 grams of fat and 20 milligrams of salt.

These potato chips accounted for 10 percent of the recommended fat allowance.
They accounted for 5 percent of the recommended salt allowance.

The statements that tell what someone thinks, feels, or believes are:

But regular potato chips taste better.

You shouldn't waste your money on reduced-fat chips.

Read this story about a girl with two homes. As you read, ask yourself, "Which statements can be proved? Which statements cannot be proved?" Then answer the questions.

My name is Lorraine Aristide. I think of myself as an international girl. This is because I have two homes, both of which I love, even though they are very different from each other. My American home is with my aunt in Boston, Massachusetts. We live in the best two-bedroom apartment in the city. My other home is with my mother, in Port-au-Prince, Haiti. There we live in a bright stucco house. I spend nine months of the year in Boston and the three summer months in Port-au-Prince. Summer is the best time to stay in Port-au-Prince. Each time I leave one home for the other, I am always happy to return. Hundreds of miles and many cultural differences separate my two homes. But this is the best way to live. I see myself as both American and Haitian at the same time.

1. Which statement is a *fact*?
   Ⓐ   We live in the best two-bedroom apartment in the city.
   Ⓑ   Summer is the best time to stay in Port-au-Prince.
   Ⓒ   I think of myself as an international girl.
   Ⓓ   I spend nine months of the year in Boston and the three summer months in Port-au-Prince.

2. Which clue word signals an *opinion* of Lorraine's about living in two countries?
   Ⓐ   think
   Ⓑ   always
   Ⓒ   believe
   Ⓓ   best

Work with a Partner

- Talk about your answers to the questions.
- Tell why you chose your answers.
- Then talk about what you have learned so far about distinguishing between fact and opinion.

REVIEW

Facts are statements that can be checked or proved. Opinions are statements that tell what someone thinks, feels, or believes.

- To determine if a statement is a fact, ask yourself, "Can this statement be checked or proved?"
- To determine if a statement is an opinion, ask yourself, "Does this statement tell what someone thinks, feels, or believes?"
- Look for clue words that signal an opinion, such as *think, feel, believe, seem, always, never, all, none, most, least, greatest, best,* and *worst.*

Read this article about a news organization called *Children's Express*. As you read, think about which statements are facts and which statements are opinions. Then answer the questions.

Children's Express was a news organization for young journalists. These journalists were age 8 through 18. They researched and reported on issues and events of the day. Topics include family life, education, children's rights, and the environment.

Children's Express had a unique mission. It gave young people an opportunity to express themselves about major issues. This happens rarely in our society. Decisions that directly impact children are often made without their input. As one young journalist said, "A solitary voice is not enough to make adults' heads turn. What we need are the voices of many children, united as one."

The articles written by young people for *Children's Express* appeared in major newspapers throughout the United States and England. *Children's Express* no longer exists, but we need more organizations like it.

3. Which statement is a *fact*?
   Ⓐ *Children's Express* had a unique mission.
   Ⓑ This happens rarely in our society today.
   Ⓒ *Children's Express* was a news organization for young journalists.
   Ⓓ A solitary voice is not enough to make adults' heads turn.

4. Which of these tells what someone thinks, feels, or believes?
   Ⓐ These journalists were age 8 through 18.
   Ⓑ What we need are the voices of many children, united as one.
   Ⓒ They researched and reported on issues and events of the day.
   Ⓓ Topics included family life, education, children's rights, and the environment.

Which Answer Is Correct and Why?

Look at the answer choices for each question.
Read why each answer choice is correct or not correct.

3. Which statement is a *fact*?

   Ⓐ *Children's Express* had a unique mission.

   This answer is not correct because it cannot be proved that *Children's Express* had a unique mission. Most likely, there have been other news organizations that publish young journalists' work.

   Ⓑ This happens rarely in our society today.

   This answer is not correct because it tells what the writer thinks about children's not having a voice in society.

   ● *Children's Express* was a news organization for young journalists.

   This answer is correct because you can prove this statement is true by finding information about the organization in a library or online.

   Ⓓ A solitary voice is not enough to make adults' heads turn.

   This answer is not correct because this statement cannot be proved to be true for all adults.

4. Which of these tells what someone thinks, feels, or believes?

   Ⓐ These journalists were age 8 through 18.

   This answer is not correct because you can prove this statement to be true by finding information about the ages of the journalists in a library or online.

   ● What we need are the voices of many children, united as one.

   This answer is correct because it tells what someone thinks or feels. This statement is an opinion. It cannot be proved in reference sources or by experts or with statistics.

   Ⓒ They researched and reported on issues and events of the day.

   This answer is not correct because you can prove this statement is true by researching information about how the journalists worked on their articles, as well as what issues they reported on.

   Ⓓ Topics included family life, education, children's rights, and the environment.

   This answer is not correct because you can prove this statement is true by researching information about the kind of topics the journalists wrote about.

MORE TO KNOW

- Facts often contain numbers, dates, or ages. Facts might include specific information about a person, place, or thing.

- Distinguishing between fact and opinion in persuasive writing can be difficult. Facts are often used to support opinions. An opinion is often based on fact, but it is still an opinion.

- Opinions deal with things that cannot be verified. Some opinions are written to sound like facts, but if you cannot verify what you read, it is probably an opinion.

Read this article about the giant squid. Then answer the questions.

Of all sea creatures, the giant squid is the most mysterious. Related to the octopus, this huge mollusk is found in each of the world's oceans. Yet it is rarely seen because it swims thousands of feet underwater.

People have known about the elusive giant squid since ancient times. Sightings by sailors spawned myths about sea monsters. In the 1800s, Jules Verne wrote about a giant squid in the story *Twenty Thousand Leagues Under the Sea.*

Throughout the twentieth century, scientists studied only remains of dead giant squid. Then, in 2004, Japanese researchers captured the first images of a live one. After this feat, science writer Richard Ellis commented, "I think it's wonderful that we've finally got a picture of a living giant squid." Two years later, Japanese scientists caught a live giant squid, and U.S. government scientists caught one in the Gulf of Mexico in 2009. These amazing discoveries have provided valuable information.

It is known that a giant squid can grow to be huge. Because of its impressive size, it has few predators. But, it is an effective hunter. A giant squid has eight arms and two feeding tentacles covered with suction cups. With its tentacles, a giant squid catches fish, shrimp, and other prey. Also, giant squid have the largest eyes in the animal kingdom. These eyes help them see in the murky ocean. Imagine an eye the size of a basketball!

Over time, scientists have learned much about giant squid. However, many questions still remain.

5. Which statement can be proved?
   - Ⓐ The giant squid is a member of the mollusk family.
   - Ⓑ Giant squid are fascinating creatures.
   - Ⓒ Japanese scientists have the best research equipment.
   - Ⓓ Researchers should learn more about squid.

6. Which statement expresses an *opinion*?
   - Ⓐ The giant squid has eight arms and two feeding tentacles.
   - Ⓑ "I think it's wonderful that we've finally got a picture of a living giant squid."
   - Ⓒ The giant squid lives in every ocean in the world.
   - Ⓓ In 2004, Japanese researchers captured the first images of a live giant squid.

7. Which clue word signals an *opinion* in paragraph 3?
   - Ⓐ always
   - Ⓑ believe
   - Ⓒ think
   - Ⓓ better

8. Which of these tells something that can be proved?
   - Ⓐ More scientists need to study giant squid.
   - Ⓑ Giant squid have the largest eyes in the animal kingdom.
   - Ⓒ Efforts to learn about giant squid have been remarkable.
   - Ⓓ The giant squid has a bizarre appearance.

Read this letter to the editor about the city zoo. Then answer the questions.

All voters should choose in favor of Proposal 3. This proposal is for a one-half percent increase on property taxes. These funds will go directly to support the city zoo. The average taxpayer will see an increase of less than $10 per year. By supporting this proposal, we will be giving little to gain much. We will also be doing our part to save animals and preserve the environment.

The city zoo serves a vital global function. Its work is essential to the survival of several endangered species. Zoologists at the city zoo breed two species of American animals. These are the whooping crane and the black-footed ferret. The survival of these animals in the wild has been threatened. Their natural habitat has been seriously compromised. In addition, the zoo supports conservation projects in Africa, India, and Indonesia. These projects are designed to prevent zoos from becoming the only home for many rare species of tigers and monkeys. All citizens should support these efforts. The zoo also educates visitors about these issues and raises funds. The city zoo's education programs are the best in the nation.

By supporting the zoo, we can protect worldwide efforts to ensure the survival of endangered species and the conservation of wilderness. I urge citizens to vote in favor of Proposal 3 on Tuesday.

Maria Amalfitano
Brighton Hills

9. Which statement is a *fact* from the letter?
   Ⓐ The average taxpayer will see an increase of less than $10 per year.
   Ⓑ By supporting this proposal, we will be giving little to gain much.
   Ⓒ All voters should choose in favor of Proposal 3.
   Ⓓ We will also be doing our part to save animals and preserve the environment.

10. Which statement is an *opinion*?
   Ⓐ Zoologists at the city zoo breed two species of American animals.
   Ⓑ This proposal is for a one-half percent increase on property taxes.
   Ⓒ The zoo also educates visitors about these issues and raises funds.
   Ⓓ The city zoo serves a vital global function.

11. Which of the following is a *fact*?
   Ⓐ By supporting this proposal, we will be giving little to gain much.
   Ⓑ The zoo supports conservation projects in Africa, India, and Indonesia.
   Ⓒ The city zoo's education programs are the best in the nation.
   Ⓓ All citizens should support these efforts.

12. Which of these expresses an *opinion* of the letter writer?
   Ⓐ Their natural habitat is already gone.
   Ⓑ These additional monies will go directly to support the city zoo.
   Ⓒ Zoologists at the city zoo breed two species of American animals.
   Ⓓ All voters should choose in favor of Proposal 3.

TEST TIPS

- A test question about distinguishing between fact and opinion may ask you to determine if a statement is a fact or an opinion. If a statement can be proved, it is a fact. If it cannot, it is an opinion.

- To recognize a *fact*, read each answer choice and ask yourself, "Can this statement be proved?"

- To recognize an *opinion*, read each answer choice and ask yourself, "Does this statement tell what someone thinks, feels, or believes?" Also, look in the answer choices for clue words that signal an opinion.

Read this retelling of a Vietnamese folktale. Then answer questions about the folktale. Choose the best answer for Numbers 13 and 14.

The Clever Little Worm

One day long ago, there was a fisherman who fished every day at the same spot on the riverbank. On this particular day, at the end of his hook dangled a frightened little worm. As every fish swam by, the poor little worm knew that it was only a matter of time before he would be eaten.

When one especially hungry fish swam by and stared at the worm, the little fellow stayed as still as he could. But when the fish opened his wide mouth, the little worm cried out, "Mr. Fish! You are in danger yourself! Do you see what is above me?"

The fish closed his jaws and asked, "What? I don't see anything but a tasty worm."

"Look closer, Mr. Fish, and you will see a fishing line. There is a man at the end of the line who is trying to catch you." The worm tried to look as sad and pathetic as he could, and then went on, "I have no care myself about leaving this world and my miserable life spent crawling and hiding beneath the ground where it is always dark and lonely." The worm choked back tears as he added, "But you, Mr. Fish, you are so strong and handsome. Your scales shine like diamonds under the water. I would hate to see you caught and cooked and served up on a dinner plate. I cannot let that happen, Mr. Fish." The worm then began sobbing uncontrollably, his tiny body trembling all over.

The fish was taken aback by all the worm had to say. He did not like the idea of being served up on a dinner plate, so he took a long last look at the worm and then swam away.

Just as soon as the hungry fish disappeared, another fish swam by. He, too, was ready to open his wide mouth when the little worm began telling him the same story he had told the first fish. The second fish eventually swam away, too. And so, this happened again and again until the fisherman became frustrated that there were no fish on his hook. He pulled his line from the water, removed the worm from the hook, and tossed the worm behind him. The little worm quickly burrowed into the soil and disappeared forever.

13. Which of these is a *fact*?

Ⓐ Earthworms do not make good bait.

Ⓑ The fisherman used an earthworm for bait.

Ⓒ All earthworms are clever.

Ⓓ Fishermen should never use an earthworm for bait.

14. Which statement is an *opinion* expressed in the story?

Ⓐ "Do you see what is above me?"

Ⓑ "Look closer, Mr. Fish, and you will see a fishing line."

Ⓒ "There is a man at the end of the line who is trying to catch you."

Ⓓ "But you, Mr. Fish, you are so strong and handsome."

Read this article about an African leader. Then answer questions about the article. Choose the best answer for Numbers 15 and 16.

Kwame Nkrumah believed in freedom, not just for the people of his own country, but for all Africans. Even after he had lost the support of the people of Ghana and was forced to live in exile, Nkrumah continued to fight for the cause of pan-Africanism. He was still working toward the goal of a united Africa when he died, in 1972.

When Kwame Nkrumah was born, in 1909, the country of Ghana did not exist. At that time, the country was a colony of Great Britain, known as the Gold Coast. The young Nkrumah was an excellent student. He later studied in the United States and England.

When he returned to the Gold Coast, Nkrumah became active in the movement to bring freedom to Africa. He was arrested several times for his participation in protests against colonial governments. While he was imprisoned following one arrest, Nkrumah ran for parliament and won. The British were forced to set him free so that he could lead the government as prime minister. He continued to serve as prime minister until 1957, when the Gold Coast finally achieved independence. Shortly after its independence, he was elected president.

As the president of the new nation, renamed Ghana, after the ancient West African kingdom, Nkrumah set to work to build a strong nation. He began a series of ambitious building projects, including the Akosombo Dam and the Black Star Monument. Akosombo Dam is in southeastern Ghana, on the Volta River. The body of water that was formed behind the dam is known as Lake Volta. Hundreds of villages are scattered along its shores. Black Star Monument is in Accra, the nation's capital. It consists of an arch 55 feet high with a black star on top. The black star is a symbol of freedom.

Critics of Nkrumah point to these structures and call them follies. They say that the Akosombo Dam does not live up to its promise to supply Ghana with all the electricity it needs. These same critics wonder why, in a country where schoolchildren often lack books, money was spent to build the Black Star Monument.

Yet, one could wonder how many of these same critics would ask why New York City doesn't sell the Statue of Liberty for scrap metal to buy new textbooks for the city's schoolchildren. Although the Statue of Liberty and the Black Star Monument are at least 3,000 miles apart, both sing out a message of freedom to their people. It is a message that Nkrumah understood well. When Nkrumah left the United States in 1945, he passed by the Statue of Liberty. "I shall never rest," Nkrumah thought, "until I have carried your message to Africa." This messenger of American spirit stands as one of the greatest African leaders.

15. Which of the following tells an *opinion*?
   Ⓐ Nkrumah believed in freedom for his own people and all Africans.
   Ⓑ Nkrumah stands as one of the greatest African leaders.
   Ⓒ Nkrumah was born in 1909.
   Ⓓ As the president of the new nation, Nkrumah set to work to build a strong nation.

16. Which of these is a *fact*?
   Ⓐ Black Star Monument was a waste of money.
   Ⓑ New York City should sell the Statue of Liberty for scrap metal.
   Ⓒ It is important for people to have symbols of freedom.
   Ⓓ Nkrumah was responsible for a series of building projects.

Distinguishing Between Fact and Opinion **101**

Read this article about Chinese immigration to the United States. Then answer questions about the article. Choose the best answer for Numbers 1 through 6.

Land of the Gold Mountain

In 1849, cries of "Gold! Gold! Gold!" rang out in California. These cries reached China, where the poor longed for a better life. Hoping to strike it rich too, many poor Chinese left their country for America, which they called "the land of the golden mountain."

Within three years, 24,000 Chinese workers had come to America to work in the gold mines. They often borrowed money from brokers to pay for their ship passage to California. Most Chinese workers arrived in San Francisco, California. Agents for the gold-mine owners met the Chinese workers at the San Francisco docks and brought them to the mines near Sacramento.

The owners of the gold mine were pleased with the Chinese workers. They almost never complained about the long hours and hard work. They also toiled for lower wages than American workers. This meant that mine owners could keep more of their profits by hiring Chinese workers. This practice was unfair.

When American mine workers realized that they were losing jobs to the Chinese, they were furious. For the next several years, American workers used violence to drive Chinese workers from the mining camps. Violence is always wrong. Eventually, the emperor of China did not allow migration to the United States.

In time, work in the gold-mining industry had begun to wane. This decrease occurred around the same time that construction of the transcontinental railroad began. Many additional workers were needed to complete the extensive project. By a treaty in 1868, the U.S. ambassador promised the emperor of China that the Chinese immigrants would receive the same rights as American citizens. The emperor agreed to allow more Chinese to immigrate to the United States.

As a result, ten thousand more Chinese workers immigrated to work on the railroad. They performed difficult and dangerous labor. They removed debris, carried timber, laid railroad track, and blasted rock. The Chinese built the track from the West toward the East, struggling across desert and through mountains. Other workers built the track toward the West. The two groups joined their tracks in Utah in 1869. People could now ride the rails from New York to San Francisco.

No longer needed in the gold mines or for the railroad, the Chinese were released from their work. They found new employment by starting businesses or working as servants or on farms. However, they once again faced hostility from workers, as well as the government. By 1882, Congress had passed the Chinese Exclusion Act, ending Chinese immigration to America. For the next 60 years, no Chinese settled in the United States. In 1943, the U.S. Congress rescinded the act, and the Chinese were allowed to enter the country once again.

Finding Word Meaning
in Context

Drawing Conclusions
and Making Inferences

Distinguishing Between
Fact and Opinion

Finding Word Meaning in Context

1. In paragraph 3, *toiled* means
   - Ⓐ "worked for high wages."
   - Ⓑ "performed difficult work."
   - Ⓒ "mined for gold."
   - Ⓓ "worked as a slave."

Drawing Conclusions and Making Inferences

4. Readers of the article could conclude that
   - Ⓐ the U.S. has always been open to Chinese immigrants.
   - Ⓑ Chinese immigrants faced few challenges in the U.S. after 1943.
   - Ⓒ Chinese immigrants endured greater injustices than any other immigrants.
   - Ⓓ in the 1800s, the U.S. allowed Chinese immigrants only because their labor was wanted.

Finding Word Meaning in Context

2. Which kind of clue hints at the meaning of the word *wane* in paragraph 5?
   - Ⓐ a synonym
   - Ⓑ an antonym
   - Ⓒ a definition
   - Ⓓ a comparison

Distinguishing Between Fact and Opinion

5. Which statement expresses an *opinion*?
   - Ⓐ Mine owners should have hired only American workers.
   - Ⓑ The Chinese mine workers worked for low wages.
   - Ⓒ American mine workers used violence to drive Chinese workers from the mining camps.
   - Ⓓ The emperor of China prevented Chinese workers from immigrating.

Drawing Conclusions and Making Inferences

3. From the article, you can figure out that
   - Ⓐ American mine workers labored for a higher wage than Chinese workers.
   - Ⓑ Chinese mine workers labored for a higher wage than American workers.
   - Ⓒ American mine workers performed worse than Chinese workers.
   - Ⓓ Chinese mine workers performed better than American workers.

Distinguishing Between Fact and Opinion

6. Which of these is a *fact* from the article?
   - Ⓐ Violence is always wrong.
   - Ⓑ The Chinese were great workers.
   - Ⓒ Chinese railroad workers built the track from the West toward the East.
   - Ⓓ This practice was unfair.

Read this science-fiction story about a dangerous voyage. Then answer questions about the story. Choose the best answer for Numbers 7 through 12.

Voyage to Merak

Quignas Waun paced the deck of the International Space Shuttle *Freedom* and gazed out at the rapidly disappearing Earth. She breathed a heavy sigh, her chestnut eyes fixed on a distant point in the southern Pacific Ocean. She watched her aboriginal home disappear slowly from view.

"Time to prepare," announced her uncle, Rigel Waun, as he emerged from a hallway, dressed in a shiny grey suit and carrying another one in his hands. Quignas sighed again, her shoulders sagging.

"You seem troubled, Quignas," said Rigel. "Worrying is a waste of time, and there's nothing to worry about," he added handing her the suit.

Quignas turned and reluctantly took the suit from his hands. It was time for the Waun family to don the suits and go to the hibernation chamber. Here they would remain in a frozen state as the *Freedom* embarked on a six-month journey to the Merak Space Station. There, Quignas's father, Durabel, would take command of the newly constructed space station in the Ursa Major System.

"But I am worried, Uncle," Quignas said, as she inspected her suit carefully. She fingered the seams, looking for any defects or weaknesses in the stitching. "We've trained for this mission for a long time. I knew that someday, we would embark on a new life out there." Quignas motioned into the darkness of space that cascaded beyond the ship. "But, now that the moment has arrived, I don't believe that I'm ready."

Rigel's eyebrows shot up. He had not expected to hear an expression of doubt from his niece. "Are you fearful of what will happen next?" he asked.

Quignas nodded.

"We all are," Rigel said, chuckling slightly. "I always feel afraid when I am about to begin something new, too. But what we are doing isn't entirely new. We've had lots of practice."

Quignas shrugged. "I know, but I'm terrified of the thought of being asleep for six months."

Rigel nodded. "Like I said, we've had lots of practice. Remember, you've spent an equivalent of eight months sleeping in the hibernation unit. Although it was spread out over three years, you know what it feels like. You also understand that it is all over in a nanosecond."

"I suppose," Quignas said. "I just hope that when I wake up, I like what I find."

"Remember, I have already visited Merak," Rigel said. "It's a wonderful place. There are lots of kids your age. And there's plenty to do, including your favorite sport, holographic basketball. There's a whole arena dedicated entirely to the sport. I think that once you arrive in Merak, your old home will be nothing more than a pleasant, and distant, memory."

Finding Word Meaning in Context

7. In the story, what is the best meaning for *defects*?

   Ⓐ "shortages"

   Ⓑ "flaws"

   Ⓒ "stains"

   Ⓓ "scrapes"

Drawing Conclusions and Making Inferences

10. The story says that Rigel's eyebrows shot up. This means that Rigel was

   Ⓐ excited.

   Ⓑ fearful.

   Ⓒ upset.

   Ⓓ surprised.

Finding Word Meaning in Context

8. You can tell that *nanosecond* refers to

   Ⓐ a period of eight months.

   Ⓑ a short period of time.

   Ⓒ a time of training.

   Ⓓ a period of three years.

Distinguishing Between Fact and Opinion

11. Which statement from the story expresses a *fact*?

   Ⓐ "I just hope when I wake up that I like what I find."

   Ⓑ "Everyone feels afraid after they start something new."

   Ⓒ "Worrying is a waste of time."

   Ⓓ "Remember, I have already visited Merak."

Drawing Conclusions and Making Inferences

9. Readers can conclude that Quignas

   Ⓐ has never been in a hibernation unit before.

   Ⓑ will return to her aboriginal home after the mission.

   Ⓒ has been training for the mission for about three years.

   Ⓓ will take command of a newly constructed space station.

Distinguishing Between Fact and Opinion

12. Which clue word signals an *opinion* in the last paragraph?

   Ⓐ believe

   Ⓑ think

   Ⓒ always

   Ⓓ seem

IDENTIFYING AUTHOR'S PURPOSE

PART ONE: Think About the Strategy

What Is Author's Purpose?

Authors write for a reason. Everything you read has a purpose.
The author's purpose is either to describe, to entertain, to explain, or to persuade.

Write what you think the author's purpose is for writing each of the following.
Tell if the author's purpose is to describe, to entertain, to explain, or to persuade.

1 A magazine article about technology over the past ten years

The author's purpose is to _____.

2 A humorous story about an embarrassing experience

The author's purpose is to _____.

3 An advertisement for a spring clothing sale

The author's purpose is to _____.

4 A blog entry about a visit to a beautiful lake

The author's purpose is to _____.

Work with a Partner

- Take turns talking about some of the programs you see on TV. Think about things such as dramas, educational programs, science shows, commercials, and so on.
- Together, see if you can identify the purpose of each TV presentation.

How Do You Find Author's Purpose?

Every reading passage is written for a reason. When you read, ask yourself, "What does the author want me to know?" Your answer will help you figure out the author's purpose.

Read this passage about Puritans. See if you can figure out the author's purpose.

> The Puritans who settled in New England colonies had strict rules about their clothing. They did not wear bright colors or clothing with ruffles or lace. They also wore no jewelry. Women wore long-sleeved gray dresses with large white collars and cuffs. They also wore a white apron and cap. Men wore baggy pants made of leather and long, woolen stockings. Children dressed in the same styles as their parents.

1. Think about what the author wants you to know.

   First, let's narrow down the choices.
   Look at the chart below.

2. Check "yes" or "no" for each choice. You can check "yes" only once in this chart.

	Yes	No	
Does the passage mostly give descriptive details about a particular person, place, or thing?			Describe
Does the passage tell a humorous story or teach a lesson?			Entertain
Does the passage give facts about something or tell how to do something?			Explain
Does the passage try to get you to do or buy something?			Persuade

3. Write the choice that has a check mark under "yes."

_____

WHAT TO KNOW

All authors write for a reason. The reason an author writes something is called the author's purpose. When you figure out why a reading passage was written, you are **identifying the author's purpose**. Authors write for one of four reasons—to describe, to entertain, to explain or inform, or to persuade.

- If a reading passage contains many descriptive details about a person, place, or thing, the author's purpose is to **describe**.

- If a reading passage is enjoyable to read, tells a personal story, or uses a story to teach a lesson, the author's purpose is to **entertain**.

- If a reading passage provides facts about a particular subject or tells readers how to do something, the author's purpose is to **explain** or **inform**.

- If a reading passage contains many opinions or tries to get readers to do something, buy something, or believe something, the author's purpose is to **persuade**.

Read this article about bicycles. As you read, think about why the author probably wrote the article.

There are several types of bicycles available today. There are mountain bikes, racing bikes, hybrid bikes, and cruiser bikes. The mountain bike, with its sturdy frame and wide, tough-treaded tires, is the ideal bike for riding on rough terrain. The racing bike, with its lightweight frame, narrow tires, and drop handlebars, is designed for long-distance rides on smooth, paved roads. The hybrid bike is a cross between the mountain bike and the racing bike. It's suited for leisure riding and commuting. Best for short rides, the cruiser bike is the workhorse of today's bike, similar to old single-speed bikes.

The author probably wrote the article to provide information.
The author's purpose is to inform readers about different kinds of bicycles.

Read this article about Japan's Himeji Castle. As you read, try to figure out the author's purpose for writing the article. Then answer the questions.

Himeji Castle in Japan is a popular site. It is located on a hill above the Harima plains. Its construction began in 1346 and was completed by 1618. The exterior of the castle features massive stone foundations and curving tile roofs. At the roof corners, statues of tiger-headed fish stand guard.

Unlike other medieval castles, Himeji Castle is made of wood. Shimmering white-plastered wood walls give it the appearance of a bird about to take flight. For this reason, it was nicknamed White Heron Castle.

In wartime, Himeji Castle was well defended by three moats, many gates, and strong outer walls. Holes shaped like circles, rectangles, squares, or triangles were cut into the walls. Each hole was created for a different kind of weapon. For example, archers would have shot arrows from the rectangular holes.

The castle's interior was also cleverly designed to protect its inhabitants. The castle has a main tower and three smaller ones. The lord and his family lived in the main tower. The route to the main tower is a complicated maze. It consists of winding passageways, hidden doors, and dead ends meant to confuse intruders. It is no wonder that this exquisite castle was never invaded—except by tourists.

1. The author wrote the article in order to
   Ⓐ explain about warfare in medieval Japan.
   Ⓑ describe Himeji Castle in Japan.
   Ⓒ persuade readers to learn more about Japanese history.
   Ⓓ entertain readers with a suspenseful story.

2. You know your answer to question 1 is correct because the article mainly
   Ⓐ provides facts or tells readers how to do something.
   Ⓑ contains many details that describe a person, place, or thing.
   Ⓒ tries to convince readers of something.
   Ⓓ relates an enjoyable story.

Work with a Partner

- Talk about your answers to the questions.
- Tell why you chose your answers.
- Then talk about what you have learned so far about identifying author's purpose.

REVIEW

Authors write for four main reasons—to describe, to entertain, to explain or inform, or to persuade.

- As you read, ask yourself, "Does the reading passage contain many details that describe a person, place, or thing?" If so, the author's purpose is to describe.

- As you read, ask yourself, "Does the reading passage contain a humorous or personal story? Does the author use a story to teach a lesson?" If so, the author's purpose is to entertain.

- As you read, ask yourself, "Does the reading passage provide facts or tell readers how to do something?" If so, the author's purpose is to explain or inform.

- As you read, ask yourself, "Does the reading passage contain opinions that try to convince readers to do something, buy something, or believe something?" If so, the author's purpose is to persuade.

Read this notice about wearing a bicycle helmet. As you read, ask yourself, "Why did the author probably write this notice?" Then answer the questions.

Wear Your Helmet

Always wear your helmet whenever you ride your bicycle, even if it's just a short ride around the block. Wearing a bicycle helmet may not be cool. But it is essential to your health and safety. If you should crash and fall to the pavement, your helmet will protect your head from a serious injury. The most common head injury is a concussion, which can lead to a coma or even death. Riding your bicycle without a helmet is simply not worth the risk of injury or death.

3. The main purpose of the notice is to
   Ⓐ describe what a bicycle helmet looks like.
   Ⓑ explain how a bicycle helmet protects.
   Ⓒ persuade readers to wear a bicycle helmet.
   Ⓓ entertain readers with a story about a bicycle helmet.

4. You know your answer to question 3 is correct because the notice mainly
   Ⓐ contains many details that describe a person, place, or thing.
   Ⓑ provides facts or tells readers how to do something.
   Ⓒ tries to convince readers of something.
   Ⓓ relates an enjoyable story.

110 Identifying Author's Purpose

Which Answer Is Correct and Why?

**Look at the answer choices for each question.
Read why each answer choice is correct or not correct.**

3. The main purpose of the notice is to

   Ⓐ **describe what a bicycle helmet looks like.**

   This answer is not correct because the reading passage does not contain any details that describe a bicycle helmet.

   Ⓑ **explain how a bicycle helmet protects.**

   This answer is not correct because the reading passage does not contain facts or other information that explain how a bicycle helmet protects.

   ⬤ **persuade readers to wear a bicycle helmet.**

   This answer is correct because the reading passage contains several of the author's opinions about why bicycle helmets are important.

   Ⓓ **entertain readers with a story about a bicycle helmet.**

   This answer is not correct because the reading passage does not contain a humorous or personal story, nor does it use a story to teach a lesson.

4. You know your answer to question 3 is correct because the notice mainly

   Ⓐ **contains many details that describe a person, place, or thing.**

   This answer is not correct because the notice does not contain details that describe bicycle helmets.

   Ⓑ **provides facts or tells readers how to do something.**

   This answer is not correct because, even though the notice does contain facts about bicycle helmets and concussions, this information is used to support the author's opinion about wearing a bicycle helmet.

   ⬤ **tries to convince readers of something.**

   This answer is correct because the notice contains the opinions of the author. The author uses these opinions to try to make readers wear a helmet when riding a bicycle.

   Ⓓ **relates an enjoyable story.**

   This answer is not correct because the notice does not contain a humorous or personal story, nor does it use a story to teach a lesson.

> **MORE TO KNOW**
>
> Different reading passages are written for different purposes. Knowing the kind of passage you are reading often helps you identify the author's purpose.
>
> • Articles are usually written to describe or explain. Some articles describe a person, place, or thing. Others explain something, such as how the water cycle works or what is the latest fad.
>
> • Directions are written to explain.
>
> • Personal stories, riddles, and poetry are written to entertain.
>
> • Ads and articles in which an opinion is stated are written to persuade.

Read this article about mosaics. Then answer the questions.

Mosaics are pictures that are formed by arranging small pieces of glass, stone, or other materials. Fixed against a hard surface, these individual pieces combine to form a whole.

Thousands of years ago, mosaic art developed in Egypt, Persia, India, and other parts of the world. In Mexico, Aztecs made colorful mosaic masks. In ancient Rome and Greece, mosaics decorated walls, floors, and ceilings of homes and public buildings.

Exquisite mosaics were discovered in the ruins of Pompeii, an Italian city that was buried under ash after the eruption of Mount Vesuvius in 79 A.D. One floor mosaic in Pompeii depicts a battle between the armies of Alexander the Great and Darius III. More than one million colored tiles were arranged to portray a vivid scene of lifelike soldiers and horses.

Making your own mosaic is a fun arts-and-crafts project. You'll need these materials: heavy cardboard, a pencil or colored marker, glue, and an assortment of colorful seeds and beans such as pumpkin seeds and pinto beans. If you prefer, use broken tile, pebbles, sea glass, or shells in place of seeds and beans. Follow these numbered directions.

1. First, draw a simple pattern or picture on the cardboard.
2. Then choose seeds and beans and arrange them on the cardboard.
3. Next, glue the seeds and beans on the cardboard, following your design.
4. Allow your mosaic to dry.

5. The author's purpose in paragraph 2 is to
   Ⓐ describe mosaic masks.
   Ⓑ entertain readers with a story about making a mosaic.
   Ⓒ persuade readers to decorate their homes with mosaics.
   Ⓓ explain ways in which mosaics were created in ancient civilizations.

6. What is the author's purpose in paragraph 3?
   Ⓐ to convince readers to travel to Italy
   Ⓑ to explain how a volcano erupts
   Ⓒ to describe an example of mosaics found in Pompeii
   Ⓓ to entertain readers with an adventure story

7. What is the author's purpose in the last paragraph?
   Ⓐ to entertain readers with a creative story
   Ⓑ to describe a mosaic made of sea glass
   Ⓒ to tell readers how to make their own mosaic
   Ⓓ to persuade readers to take an arts-and-crafts class

8. The article was written mainly to
   Ⓐ persuade readers to make mosaics.
   Ⓑ inform readers about mosaic art.
   Ⓒ describe examples of Greek mosaics.
   Ⓓ explain how mosaics were made in ancient times.

Read this movie review. Then answer the questions.

Deranged Dinosaurs Destroy Dallas

Last night, I attended the opening of the latest action-adventure film from director Randy Rock. Rock spent over 50 million dollars creating *Deranged Dinosaurs Destroy Dallas*. This was money poorly spent.

Deranged Dinosaurs Destroy Dallas does open with fantastic special effects. In the first scene, T. Rex, the antihero, munches on a transformer tower in downtown Dallas as 100 Texas Rangers, led by Commander Steele (played by actor Brad Buckley), stand by helplessly. Nothing they try can stop T. Rex. He marches through the city, trampling cars, buildings, and trains while citizens flee in horror.

Unfortunately, this seven-minute scene is the best the movie has to offer. Not even the dazzling special effects can save this movie. The story line is weak and predictable. Half of the audience left the theater during the first hour. The dialogue is so ridiculous that most audience members laughed when Commander Steele fell victim to the jaws of T. Rex.

Deranged Dinosaurs Destroy Dallas is now playing at the Metro Multiplex Theater. But save yourself some money, and wait a month for the video to arrive at your local rental store.

9. What is the author's purpose in paragraph 2?
   - Ⓐ to inform readers about a new movie that just opened
   - Ⓑ to describe the opening scene of a movie
   - Ⓒ to entertain readers with background information about the movie's director
   - Ⓓ to persuade readers to see the whole movie

10. The author's purpose in paragraph 3 is to
   - Ⓐ describe how audience members reacted to the movie.
   - Ⓑ explain why the movie is not worth seeing.
   - Ⓒ entertain readers with a story about the audience's reaction to the movie.
   - Ⓓ convince readers to view the movie if they like humor.

11. The author's purpose in the last paragraph is to
   - Ⓐ persuade readers to view the movie at home, rather than at the theater.
   - Ⓑ inform readers that the movie is not worth viewing at all.
   - Ⓒ describe in detail how to best view the movie.
   - Ⓓ entertain readers with an amusing joke.

12. The review was written mainly to
   - Ⓐ inform readers about a new movie.
   - Ⓑ entertain readers with an amusing story about a new movie.
   - Ⓒ persuade readers that a new movie is not worth seeing at a movie theater.
   - Ⓓ describe how a new movie was made.

**TEST
TIPS**

- A test question about identifying the author's purpose may ask you why an author probably wrote a particular reading passage. This kind of question is asking about the purpose of the entire reading passage.

- A test question about identifying the author's purpose may ask you why a particular paragraph was written. This kind of question is asking about only one part of the reading passage.

- A test question about identifying the author's purpose may ask you what you think the author wants readers to know. To help you answer this type of test question, think about why the author probably wrote the reading passage.

Read this retelling of a Hispanic folktale from the Southwest. Then answer questions about the folktale. Choose the best answer for Numbers 13 and 14.

When the world was still young, there were only four basic elements on the earth—Water, Fire, Wind, and Honor. The elements all worked together to create the world and the heavens above. When their work was done, they decided to break out on their own, each seeking a different path.

As they began their parting, Water spoke to the other elements and said, "Now that our work is done and we have decided to go our own way, always know that you can call upon me should you ever need to. All you have to do is look at the oceans and the lakes and you will find me."

Fire then spoke to the others and said, "You can call upon me as well should you ever need to. All you need to do is look to the power and strength of the sun."

Wind spoke next and said, "Should any of you need me at any time, you will find me in the sky among the birds and the clouds."

Honor spoke last and said, "Hold onto the bond I have given you, for if ever you lose me, you will never find me again."

13. The author's purpose in the first paragraph is to
   Ⓐ convince readers that the four elements are real.
   Ⓑ entertain readers with a joke about the four elements.
   Ⓒ provide background information about the four elements.
   Ⓓ describe the origins of a story.

14. The main purpose of the folktale is to
   Ⓐ explain facts about the four elements.
   Ⓑ entertain readers with a story that teaches a lesson.
   Ⓒ persuade readers to look for the elements, when needed.
   Ⓓ describe for readers where the four elements are found.

Read this article about elderly dogs. Then answer questions about the article. Choose the best answer for Numbers 15 and 16.

Elderly Dogs with Alzheimer's Disease

One survey found that 62 percent of dogs between the ages of 11 and 16 suffer from cognitive dysfunction. This condition is a kind of canine Alzheimer's disease. Elderly dogs with cognitive dysfunction forget their house-training, have difficulty sleeping, and are less sociable. They become disoriented in their own home. Eventually they may not even recognize their owners.

Two hundred dogs with cognitive dysfunction were part of a clinical trial. They were given a human Alzheimer's drug to treat the problem. Dog owners reported that 70 percent of the dogs showed improvement in their behavior. They also seemed less distressed. This improvement, which occurred within a week to a month, gave the dogs a new lease on life.

15. What is the author's purpose in the first paragraph?
   Ⓐ to explain what cognitive dysfunction is
   Ⓑ to entertain readers with an amusing study about elderly dogs
   Ⓒ to persuade readers to have their pets checked for cognitive problems
   Ⓓ to describe cognitive problems in elderly dogs

16. The author probably wants readers to know
   Ⓐ what kinds of animals can develop a cognitive problem.
   Ⓑ how they might help a dog who has Alzheimer's disease.
   Ⓒ where to have their elderly dogs treated for cognitive problems.
   Ⓓ why elderly dogs develop cognitive dysfunction.

What Is Figurative Language?

Has anyone ever told you that something would be a piece of cake? If so, that person used figurative language to tell you that something would be easy to accomplish. Figurative language is the use of words to mean something different from their usual dictionary meaning.

1 Read this sentence.

> You'll have to work very hard to get that floor clean.

2 Now read the next sentence. It uses different words, but has the same meaning as the first sentence.

> You'll have to use a lot of elbow grease to get that floor clean.

3 Write which sentence is more interesting, the first one or the second one. Tell why you think this is so.

_____

_____

_____

_____

Work with a Partner

- Talk about some of the words you have used or heard that have a meaning different from their usual meaning. A relative might say, "You are the apple of my eye." That means you are one of your relative's favorite people.
- See how many examples of figurative language you can think of.

How Do You Understand Figurative Language?

Usually you can use word meaning in context to help you understand figurative language. Look for context clues in a reading passage to help you figure out what new meaning the words could have. Clues might be in the sentence where the words are found. Clues may also be in the sentence just before or just after the one where the words are found.

Read this passage about a school play. See if you can figure out what the phrase *rolling in the aisles* **mean.**

> We went to our school's play last night, "The Man from Wayhill." It was supposed to be a serious story about minutemen during the American Revolution. But during the first act, the lead actor's little brother ran onto the stage. Some of the actors tried to coax him off the stage, but he ran away from them. Things turned comical as they chased him across the stage, knocking over props while the boy shouted, "Ha, ha! You can't catch me!" The audience was rolling in the aisles! The actors finally got the boy off the stage and tried to continue, but by now even they were giggling.

1. Let's narrow down the context clues to figure out what the phrase *rolling in the aisles* means.

   Look at the chart below. It shows three sentences: the one that comes before the phrase *rolling in the aisles*, the one that contains the phrase *rolling in the aisles*, and the one that comes after the phrase *rolling in the aisles*.

   Think carefully about the sentences that come before and after the phrase *rolling in the aisles*.

Things turned comical as they chased him across the stage, knocking over props while the boy shouted, "Ha, ha! You can't catch me!"	The audience was rolling in the aisles!	The actors finally got the boy off the stage and tried to continue, but by now even they were giggling.
Before		After

2. Now think about what the context clues in these sentences tell you:

   Things turned comical when a little boy ran onto the stage.
   The actors finally got the boy off the stage, but even the actors were now giggling.

   Think about what often happens if something is comical and people have started giggling.

3. The phrase *rolling in the aisles* probably means

_____

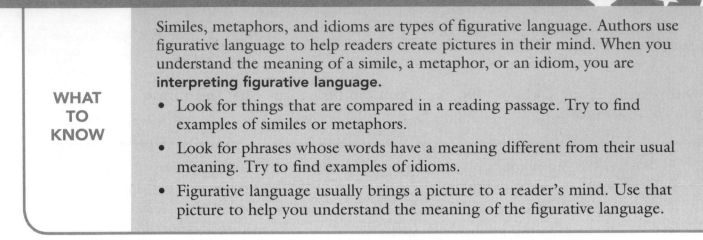

WHAT TO KNOW

Similes, metaphors, and idioms are types of figurative language. Authors use figurative language to help readers create pictures in their mind. When you understand the meaning of a simile, a metaphor, or an idiom, you are **interpreting figurative language.**

- Look for things that are compared in a reading passage. Try to find examples of similes or metaphors.
- Look for phrases whose words have a meaning different from their usual meaning. Try to find examples of idioms.
- Figurative language usually brings a picture to a reader's mind. Use that picture to help you understand the meaning of the figurative language.

Read this sentence. As you read, think about the two things being compared.

Rico's face turned as white as snow.

The two things being compared are Rico's face and snow.
The writer used a **simile** to help readers picture the color of Rico's face.
A simile uses the word *like* or *as* to compare two different things.

Read this sentence. As you read, think about the two things being compared.

Amy is a walking encyclopedia.

The two things being compared are Amy and an encyclopedia.
The writer uses a **metaphor** to show how smart Amy is.
A metaphor compares two different things but does not use the word *like* or *as*.
A metaphor says that one thing *is* another thing.

Now read this sentence. As you read, think about the meaning of the underlined phrase.

Mel passed the test <u>by the skin of his teeth</u>.

The underlined phrase means that Mel barely passed the test.
The phrase is an **idiom**.
An idiom is a phrase whose words have a meaning different from their usual meaning.

Read this web log entry about a hike through the wilderness. As you read, look for examples of figurative language.

Brad's Blog	July 18

Today, I took an early morning hike through the wilderness behind my rural home. I needed the hike to take my mind off my troubles.

As the sunlight glimmered on the horizon, songbirds warbled like a chorus of singers. The perfect morning for a hike. I headed across the meadow to the trailhead, where the edge of the wilderness meets my land. From there, I entered the dense forest, careful to stay on the trail.

After I hiked uphill for about a mile, the sound of the rushing waters of Granite Falls filled my ears. With another turn in the trail, I was on the ledge overlooking the falls. The sparkling waters cascaded over the rocks to the stream below. A sense of peace began to fill me. I sat on the ledge in quiet meditation for a few hours, and then returned home refreshed.

This made my day.

1. In the first paragraph, what does the phrase *take my mind off* mean?
   Ⓐ "become separate from"
   Ⓑ "seek a distraction from"
   Ⓒ "lose control of"
   Ⓓ "involve oneself in"

2. The writer compares the warble of the songbirds to
   Ⓐ a musician.
   Ⓑ sunlight.
   Ⓒ a chorus.
   Ⓓ a melody.

Work with a Partner

- Talk about your answers to the questions.
- Tell why you chose your answers.
- Then talk about what you have learned so far about interpreting figurative language.

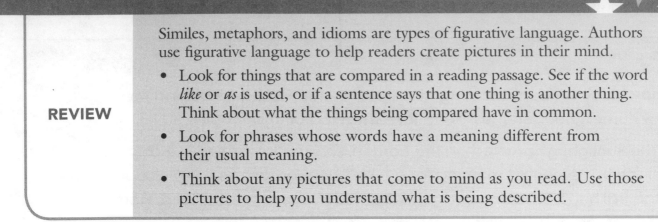

REVIEW

Similes, metaphors, and idioms are types of figurative language. Authors use figurative language to help readers create pictures in their mind.

- Look for things that are compared in a reading passage. See if the word *like* or *as* is used, or if a sentence says that one thing is another thing. Think about what the things being compared have in common.

- Look for phrases whose words have a meaning different from their usual meaning.

- Think about any pictures that come to mind as you read. Use those pictures to help you understand what is being described.

Read this part of a poem about an eagle. As you read, ask yourself, "What pictures come to mind?" Then answer the questions.

The Eagle
by Alfred, Lord Tennyson

He clasps the crag with crooked hands;
Close to the sun in lonely lands,
Ringed with the azure world, he stands.

The wrinkled sea beneath him crawls:
He watches from his mountain walls,
And like a thunderbolt he falls.

3. *The wrinkled sea beneath him crawls* describes the
   Ⓐ depth of the sea.
   Ⓑ size of the ocean below the eagle.
   Ⓒ appearance and movement of the sea.
   Ⓓ features of the mountain walls.

4. In stanza 2, the poet compares the eagle's flight to a
   Ⓐ ship.
   Ⓑ wall.
   Ⓒ mountain.
   Ⓓ thunderbolt.

Which Answer Is Correct and Why?

Look at the answer choices for each question.
Read why each answer choice is correct or not correct.

3. *The wrinkled sea beneath him crawls* describes the

Ⓐ **depth of the sea.**

This answer is not correct because the words do not suggest anything about the depth of the sea.

Ⓑ **size of the ocean below the eagle.**

This answer is not correct because the words do not suggest anything about the size of the sea below the eagle. The words describe features of the sea other than its size.

● **appearance and movement of the sea.**

This answer is correct because the surface of the sea is described with the word *wrinkled* and the slow movement of the sea is described with the word *crawls*.

Ⓓ **features of the mountain walls.**

This answer is not correct because the words describe something about the sea, not the mountain walls where the eagle is perched.

4. In stanza 2, the poet compares the eagle's flight to a

Ⓐ **ship.**

This answer is not correct because there is nothing in the poem to suggest that a ship or other vessel can be seen on the sea.

Ⓑ **wall.**

This answer is not correct because the only wall mentioned in stanza 2 is the mountain wall; and this describes where the eagle is perched, not how he is flying.

Ⓒ **mountain.**

This answer is not correct because the mountain is where the eagle is perched, not how he is flying.

● **thunderbolt.**

This answer is correct because the last line is *"And like a thunderbolt he falls."* The word *like* signals that two things are being compared in a simile.

MORE TO KNOW

- Look at the sentences near an idiom. Use context clues to help you figure out its meaning.

- Personification is another kind of figurative language. Personification gives human characteristics to animals, things, or ideas. *The stars winked in the sky.*

- Hyperbole is exaggeration used to make a point. *She leapt as high as the clouds when she heard the good news.*

Read this article about the city of Freiburg, Germany. Then answer the questions.

Germany's "Green" City

Freiburg (FRY berg) is located in Germany's Black Forest near the borders of France and Switzerland. During World War II, this city was bombed and nearly destroyed. But Freiburg is like a mythical phoenix that is consumed by fire but lives again. It has been purposefully restored.

Today, Freiburg is the environmental capital of Germany. Its practices are a blueprint for other cities. Residents recycle and compost most household waste. They live in energy-efficient homes powered by solar energy. Some people even have green roofs, or roofs covered in living plants, that keep buildings cool.

Freiburg's success makes other cities green with envy. How did Freiburg ever become so "green"? One reason is that city officials adopt policies that benefit the environment. For example, new housing must meet strict low-energy standards. Also, the old city center has a car-free pedestrian zone. One neighborhood does not allow any cars at all. In addition, the city boasts a network of bicycle paths. People bike, walk, or ride trams and buses that link business and residential areas. These efforts save energy, reduce waste, and promote a better environment.

5. The phrase *like a mythical phoenix that is consumed by fire but lives again* is an example of
   - Ⓐ personification.
   - Ⓑ hyperbole.
   - Ⓒ a simile.
   - Ⓓ a metaphor.

6. Which of these is a metaphor?
   - Ⓐ Freiburg is located in Germany's Black Forest near the borders of France and Switzerland.
   - Ⓑ Its practices are a blueprint for other cities.
   - Ⓒ One neighborhood does not allow any cars at all.
   - Ⓓ New housing must meet strict low-energy standards.

7. The phrase *green with envy* means
   - Ⓐ "furious."
   - Ⓑ "generous."
   - Ⓒ "dishonest."
   - Ⓓ "jealous."

8. *The city boasts a network of bicycle paths* is an example of
   - Ⓐ hyperbole.
   - Ⓑ personification.
   - Ⓒ a metaphor.
   - Ⓓ an idiom.

122   Interpreting Figurative Language

Read this Roman myth about a sculptor. Then answer the questions.

Pygmalion's Only Love

According to Roman myth, Pygmalion was a talented young sculptor whose only devotion was his art. He vowed to the gods that he would never fall in love with nor marry any woman. Ironically, Pygmalion set himself the task of creating the perfect statue of a woman.

Working feverishly day and night, Pygmalion crafted his statue from the smoothest of stone. When he finished, he had sculpted the finest figure of a woman yet made. But Pygmalion wasn't satisfied with his work. So he labored at the statue until, at last, he felt that he had achieved perfection. Indeed, the exquisite figure appeared to be flesh and blood rather than stone.

Now Pygmalion had devoted so much of himself to the statue of the woman that he had, much to his dismay, fallen in love with her. He was wise to the fact that she was not real, and at first it didn't matter to him. Pygmalion courted her anyway. He held her hand and kissed her, but her touch was hard and her lips cold. Eventually, Pygmalion despaired. The statue could never return his love.

Pygmalion thought that maybe if he fell in love with a beautiful young woman, he might be able to forget his creation. So Pygmalion begged Venus, the goddess of love, to help him. Venus took pity on poor Pygmalion. She granted the sad young man more than he had asked for. The next time Pygmalion gazed on the statue, she seemed even more lifelike to him. He grasped her hand, and it was warm. He touched her wrist and felt a strong pulse beating there. She was alive!

Overjoyed, Pygmalion embraced her, giving his only true love the name Galatea. Galatea whispered in his ear that she loved him too. With Venus's blessing, Pygmalion and Galatea soon married and spent many happy years together.

---

9. The phrase *working feverishly day and night* is an example of
   - (A) hyperbole.
   - (B) an idiom.
   - (C) a simile.
   - (D) personification.

10. In paragraph 3, the phrase *was wise to* means
   - (A) "was doubtful of."
   - (B) "was fully aware of."
   - (C) "was somewhat uncertain of."
   - (D) "was unwilling to admit."

11. What does *flesh and blood* refer to?
   - (A) a living human body
   - (B) a statue of a human figure
   - (C) a dead human body
   - (D) a drawing of a human figure

12. From the phrase *took pity on*, readers can tell that
   - (A) Venus thought highly of Pygmalion.
   - (B) Venus was upset by Pygmalion's devotion.
   - (C) Venus acted kindly toward Pygmalion.
   - (D) Venus felt sorry for Pygmalion.

Read this ad from a newspaper. Then answer questions about the ad. Choose the best answer for Numbers 13 and 14.

Attention Teachers, Students, and Crafters!
The Recycle Shop is now open every day
from 8:00 a.m. to 4:00 p.m.

The Recycle Shop is a gold mine for anyone with just a little imagination. Are you a teacher in the market for materials to supplement your classroom art projects or science curriculum? Are you a crafter who likes to paint T-shirts or make quilts? Or maybe you're a student working on a school project. If you are any of these, then The Recycle Shop is just the place for you! Think about all the things you can create with safe industrial leftovers. We carry everything from ribbons to rubber, tubes to bottle tops, game pieces to camera cases, as well as a variety of fabrics and paints. Come browse the barrels. Buy materials by the bagful for just a few dollars.

The Recycle Shop also carries all kinds of prefabricated items, which are sold by the piece. These range in cost between 5¢ and $2.00. Individual items include game pieces, fabric paint, foam, wooden beads, and plastic frames.

Materials sold in the shop change weekly, so drop by often. Some of things you may find this week include:

- Cardboard boxes
- Wooden shapes in a variety of sizes
- Plastic discs, bottles, cones, and lids
- Soft foam in various shapes and colors
- Assorted paper, including oak tag, craft paper, and contact paper

---

13. The words *in the market for* mean

- Ⓐ "willing to sell."
- Ⓑ "looking to buy."
- Ⓒ "able to create."
- Ⓓ "searching everywhere."

14. Which of these is a metaphor?

- Ⓐ The Recycle Shop is a gold mine . . .
- Ⓑ Come browse the barrels.
- Ⓒ Think about all the things you can create . . .
- Ⓓ . . . by the bagful for just a few dollars.

Read this selection from *The Wind in the Willows* by Kenneth Grahame. Then answer questions about the selection. Choose the best answer for Numbers 15 and 16.

A Midsummer's Night

The Willow Wren was twittering his thin little song, hidden himself in the dark selvedge of the river bank. Though it was past ten o'clock at night, the sky still clung to and retained some lingering skirts of light from the departed day; and the sullen heats of the torrid afternoon broke up and rolled away at the dispersing touch of the cool fingers of the short midsummer night. Mole lay stretched on the bank, still panting from the stress of the fierce day that had been cloudless from dawn to late sunset, and waited for his friend to return. He had been on the river with some companions, leaving the Water Rat free to keep an engagement of long standing with Otter; and he had come back to find the house dark and deserted, and no sign of Rat, who was doubtless keeping it up late with his old comrade. It was still too hot to think of staying indoors, so he lay on some cool dock leaves, and thought over the past day and its doings, and how very good they all had been.

15. The phrase *no sign of Rat* means that
    Ⓐ Rat didn't leave a message for Mole.
    Ⓑ there wasn't a sign posted about rats.
    Ⓒ there wasn't any indication that Rat had been home.
    Ⓓ Mole was upset that Rat wasn't home yet.

16. The phrase *the dispersing touch of the cool fingers of the short midsummer night* is an example of
    Ⓐ a metaphor.
    Ⓑ a simile.
    Ⓒ hyperbole.
    Ⓓ personification.

What Is Summarizing?

A summary is a short statement that tells the main points or important ideas of something you have read or watched, such as a play, a movie, or a documentary. When you restate the important ideas, you are summarizing.

1 Write the name of a movie or documentary that you watched in the past few weeks.

_____

2 Write three of the important events from the movie or documentary.

_____

_____

_____

3 Write one sentence that tells how you would answer someone who asked you what the movie or documentary was about. Include information about all the important events in your sentence.

_____

_____

_____

_____

Work with a Partner

- Take turns summarizing books, movies, or different programs you have watched on TV.
- Make sure to tell about the most important ideas in one sentence.

How Do You Know What Makes a Good Summary?

A good summary of a reading passage depends on the kind of passage you are reading. If you are reading fiction, usually you will read about a character that has a problem. Your summary should tell about the character, the problem, and the solution. If you are reading nonfiction, your summary should tell about the main idea of the passage, as well as the important points contained in the paragraphs.

Read this passage about some customs in the Middle Ages. Think about what would make a good summary of this nonfiction passage.

> In the Middle Ages, ordinary Europeans had different dining customs than we do today. They served meals on platters or in stew pots from which all the members of a household took their portions. Then diners either ate straight off the table or placed the food on trenchers. Trenchers were usually plate-like squares cut out of a loaf of stale bread. After use, bread trenchers were given to peasants or fed to dogs and pigs. Pairs of diners shared a single drinking cup unless a jug from which everyone drank was passed around the table. Some medieval diners ate with their bare hands, whereas others supplied their own knives and spoons. With the exception of Italy, the use of forks in Europe was uncommon.

1. Let's narrow down the main idea and the important points in the nonfiction passage.

   Look at the chart below.
   The first box shows the main idea. The next three boxes show the important points about the main idea.

2. Use the main idea and important points to finish the one-sentence summary in the last box.

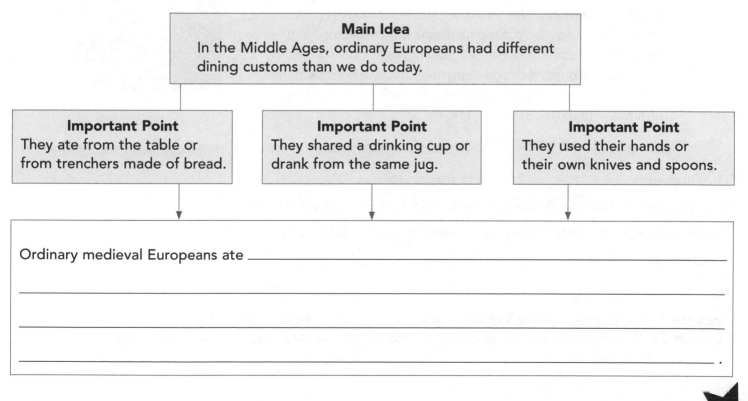

Main Idea
In the Middle Ages, ordinary Europeans had different dining customs than we do today.

Important Point
They ate from the table or from trenchers made of bread.

Important Point
They shared a drinking cup or drank from the same jug.

Important Point
They used their hands or their own knives and spoons.

Ordinary medieval Europeans ate _____

_____

_____

_____ .

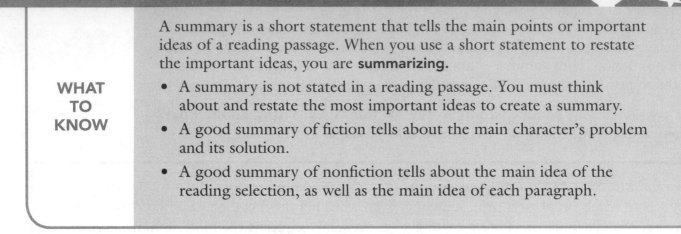

WHAT TO KNOW

A summary is a short statement that tells the main points or important ideas of a reading passage. When you use a short statement to restate the important ideas, you are **summarizing.**

- A summary is not stated in a reading passage. You must think about and restate the most important ideas to create a summary.

- A good summary of fiction tells about the main character's problem and its solution.

- A good summary of nonfiction tells about the main idea of the reading selection, as well as the main idea of each paragraph.

Read this article about therapy animals. As you read, think about the most important ideas in the article. Then think about what you might tell someone who asks what the article is about.

Therapy animals have been used in the United States since the 1970s. These animals—and their handlers—all receive special training. Then they visit hospitals, nursing homes, and other facilities.

Many kinds of animals are therapy animals. Common therapy animals include cats, dogs, monkeys, birds, pigs, and rabbits. In some places, even horses and elephants are therapy animals.

Therapy animals help with both physical and emotional problems. They can cheer people up. They can calm people down. They might help patients improve their balance and strength. For example, a stroke patient might brush a cat. This act of grooming brings enjoyment. But it also works the patient's muscles. Therapy animals can make an important difference in a patient's recovery.

The most important ideas in the article are:

Therapy animals have been used in the United States since the 1970s.

Common therapy animals include cats, dogs, monkeys, birds, pigs, and rabbits.

Therapy animals help with both physical and emotional problems.

Here is what you might tell someone who asks what the article is about:

Since the 1970s, therapy animals including cats, dogs, monkeys, birds, pigs, and rabbits have been used in the United States to help patients recover from physical and emotional problems.

Read this article about the country of Laos. As you read, think about the main idea of the reading selection, as well as the main idea of each paragraph. Then answer the questions.

Laos is a land of many divisions. It is a long, narrow country wedged between Vietnam and Thailand. The two dominant groups of people are the Lao, from the lowlands of the south, and the Hmong, from the northern highlands.

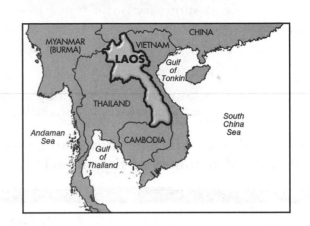

The Lao became split politically into the Royal Lao and the communist Pathet Lao. During the 1950s, civil war broke out between the two groups. By the 1960s, the Vietnam War had extended into Laos. The North Vietnamese supported the Pathet Lao, and the United States government gave assistance to the Royal Lao. The United States also enlisted Hmong help in fighting against the communists.

In 1975, the victorious Pathet Lao gained control of Laos. Fearing for their lives, thousands of Royal Lao and Hmong fled to Thailand. In time, many left the crowded refugee camps there and came to the United States.

1. What is the main idea of the article?
   Ⓐ Laos is located between Vietnam and Thailand.
   Ⓑ Laos is a land of many divisions.
   Ⓒ In 1975, the victorious Pathet Lao gained control of Laos.
   Ⓓ The Lao are split politically into the Royal Lao and the communist Pathet Lao.

2. Which of these best summarizes the article?
   Ⓐ Laos is a country located between Vietnam and Thailand.
   Ⓑ The Lao and Hmong live in different regions and hold different views.
   Ⓒ Laos is a country with geographical, cultural, and political divisions.
   Ⓓ Civil War and the Vietnam War tore up Laos.

Work with a Partner

- Talk about your answers to the questions.
- Tell why you chose your answers.
- Then talk about what you have learned so far about summarizing.

REVIEW

A summary is a short statement that tells the main points or important ideas of a reading passage.

- A summary is not stated in a reading passage. Use the most important ideas in a reading passage to create a summary.
- A good summary of fiction tells about the main character's problem and its solution.
- A good summary of nonfiction includes the main ideas of the selection.

Read this story about a girl who moved to a new home. As you read, ask yourself, "What does a good summary of fiction include?" Then answer the questions.

My New Home

When my parents first told me that we would be moving from New York City to Las Cruces, New Mexico, I doubted that I would like it. New York may be concrete, but it's the center of the universe. Las Cruces sounded like the desert, somewhere in the middle of nowhere. When they added that we would be living in a rammed earth house, I felt really apprehensive.

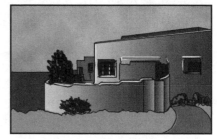

"A dirt house!" I exclaimed. "You're trading our high-rise apartment overlooking Central Park for a dusty burrow in the ground?" This was too much. Had my parents lost it?

My father tried to calm me down. "Megan, we won't be living in a burrow. Your mother, the architect, can tell you more about it." I wasn't convinced, and my face must have showed it.

So Mom explained, "A rammed earth house is like one huge adobe brick. It's made of a mixture of earth, cement, and water. The mixture is poured into a wooden frame of hollow walls and pounded until it becomes compact. The frame around the compressed walls is removed, and a roof is put on. That's the basic design of our new home."

I felt a little better when I saw the house in Soledad Canyon for myself. I had to admit that we do have a wonderful view of the Mesilla Valley, but I'm not quite ready to call it home. I still miss the city skyline and my friends at Parker Junior High too much.

3. What is Megan's problem in the story?
   Ⓐ She does not like living in the desert.
   Ⓑ She longs for the views of Central Park.
   Ⓒ She misses her home and friends in New York.
   Ⓓ She does not like living in a rammed earth house.

4. What is the best summary of the story?
   Ⓐ Megan thinks New York City is better than Las Cruces.
   Ⓑ Moving from New York to New Mexico wasn't as bad as Megan expected.
   Ⓒ Leaving New York was very difficult for Megan.
   Ⓓ Living in Las Cruces is worse than Megan expected.

Which Answer Is Correct and Why?

Look at the answer choices for each question.
Read why each answer choice is correct or not correct.

3. **What is Megan's problem in the story?**

   Ⓐ **She does not like living in the desert.**

   This answer is not correct because it does not tell the main character's problem. Megan does not state that she does not like the desert, only that she's not ready to make it home.

   Ⓑ **She longs for the views of Central Park.**

   This answer is not correct because it tells only part of the problem that Megan thought she would face when she moved.

   ⬤ **She misses her home and friends in New York.**

   This answer is correct because it tells about the main character's problem. Megan misses her home as well as her friends. This problem is stated in the last sentence of the last paragraph.

   Ⓓ **She does not like living in a rammed earth house.**

   This answer is not correct because it does not tell the main character's problem. Megan does not state that she does not like living in the earth house, only that, at first, she wasn't sure she wanted to live in one.

4. **What is the best summary of the story?**

   Ⓐ **Megan thinks New York City is better than Las Cruces.**

   This answer is not correct because it does not tell the main character's problem and its solution. This answer is an opinion of Megan's implied in the story.

   ⬤ **Moving from New York to New Mexico wasn't as bad as Megan expected.**

   This answer is correct because it tells the main character's problem and its solution. This answer tells the most important idea in the story.

   Ⓒ **Leaving New York was very difficult for Megan.**

   This answer is not correct because it does not tell the main character's problem and its solution. This answer only states one of the important ideas in the story.

   Ⓓ **Living in Las Cruces is worse than Megan expected.**

   This answer is not correct because it does not tell the main character's problem and its solution. This answer is not stated or implied in the story.

MORE TO KNOW	• A good summary of fiction often includes a statement of the theme. • A good summary of nonfiction answers *who, what, when, where, why,* and *how* questions.

Read this biographical sketch of Maya Angelou. Then answer the questions.

Maya Angelou was born Marguerite Johnson in St. Louis, Missouri, in 1928. Growing up, Angelou had a difficult home life. Her love of literature, as well as her relatives and neighbors, helped sustain her.

After graduating from high school in 1945, Maya Angelou gave birth to a son. As a single mother, she struggled to make ends meet. She held a variety of low-paying jobs. Notably, she became the first African American streetcar conductor in San Francisco.

Angelou later moved to New York City to study drama and dance. From 1954 to 1955, she performed in the opera *Porgy and Bess*. For the next five years, she performed in several plays. She then worked as a journalist in Egypt and Ghana from 1961 to 1966.

Angelou returned to the United States. She began teaching at the University of California at Los Angeles. She also began writing her first autobiographical book. By 1970, Angelou had published *I Know Why the Caged Bird Sings*. This was probably her best-known work. It describes her triumphs over the challenges of her life. By 1986, Angelou had written four more books. In one, she told of her experiences living in Ghana. In another, she told about her work in the civil-rights movement.

Maya Angelou has also written several volumes of poetry. And she has written nonfiction essays, as well as screenplays for television and film. She delivered her poem "On the Pulse of the Morning" at President Clinton's 1993 inauguration. Recently, she has been a professor of American studies at Wake Forest University, in North Carolina.

5. What is the biographical sketch mostly about?
   - Ⓐ the early life of Maya Angelou
   - Ⓑ the works of Maya Angelou
   - Ⓒ the career of Maya Angelou
   - Ⓓ the achievements of Maya Angelou

6. Which of these is *fact* from the biographical sketch?
   - Ⓐ Maya Angelou is the most talented writer of the twentieth century.
   - Ⓑ Maya Angelou overcame the struggles in her life.
   - Ⓒ Maya Angelou excels at various talents.
   - Ⓓ Maya Angelou is a universally respected and gifted writer.

7. What did Angelou do when she began teaching in California?
   - Ⓐ She traveled to Ghana as a journalist.
   - Ⓑ She published her first volume of poetry.
   - Ⓒ She began writing her first autobiographical book.
   - Ⓓ She went to New York City to study drama and dance.

8. Which of these best summarizes the biographical sketch?
   - Ⓐ Maya Angelou has excelled as a writer, performer, and professor.
   - Ⓑ Despite many hardships, Maya Angelou became highly accomplished and well-known.
   - Ⓒ Maya Angelou performed in several plays and toured around the world.
   - Ⓓ Maya Angelou has faced a variety of hardships in her life.

Read this story about a basketball game. Then answer the questions.

The basketball game had been going well for the Allentown Cougars. They were doing better than expected against their top-ranked opponents, the Freemont Marauders.

With ten minutes left to play, however, events took an abrupt turn for the Cougars. One of their key players, Anthony Roberts, had fallen and injured his head on the hardwood court. There was a hush in the stands as the team doctor, Dr. Ruiz, helped the dazed athlete to the locker room.

As the game continued without Anthony, the Marauders were able to take control. Their high scorer, Joe Fuentes, scored another basket. The Cougars' coach called a time-out. As the players gathered around the bench, Anthony emerged from the locker room. A thunderous applause erupted from the crowd as Anthony rushed to ask his coach if he could return to the game. The team doctor assured Coach Reed that Anthony had suffered only a slight bump from the fall.

Anthony's unexpected return inspired his teammates to attempt a comeback, resulting in ten unmatched points. However, as the buzzer sounded, it was apparent that the Cougars hadn't managed to score enough points to win the game.

As the Marauders began their victory celebration, Anthony lingered on the court, clearly disappointed. His teammates, however, were not. They crowded around a surprised Anthony, cheering as they lifted him up over their shoulders. Though the Cougars could not celebrate a win, they could celebrate their teammate's display of determination and team spirit.

9. What is the main problem in the story?
   - Ⓐ An injured player might affect the outcome of a basketball game.
   - Ⓑ A coach isn't sure that he should let an injured player return to a basketball game.
   - Ⓒ A basketball game might be postponed because of an injured player.
   - Ⓓ A basketball team struggles to keep its lead against an opposing team.

10. Things took an abrupt turn for the Cougars because
   - Ⓐ the doctor helped Anthony off the court.
   - Ⓑ the high scorer for the Marauders scored another basket.
   - Ⓒ a key player for the Cougars fell and injured his head.
   - Ⓓ the Cougar's coach called a time-out.

11. Why did Anthony's teammates cheer for him?
   - Ⓐ They wanted to encourage him.
   - Ⓑ They wanted to prove that winning wasn't important to them.
   - Ⓒ They wanted to show their admiration for Anthony.
   - Ⓓ They wanted to share in the Marauders' victory celebration.

12. What is the best summary of this story?
   - Ⓐ Members of a basketball team are depressed over a loss.
   - Ⓑ A basketball team plays better than expected against a top-ranked opponent.
   - Ⓒ A team loses a game but shows great team spirit.
   - Ⓓ A player makes a dramatic comeback.

TEST TIPS

- A test question about summarizing may ask you to choose the best summary of a reading passage. When you answer questions about summarizing, first determine if the reading passage is a work of fiction or nonfiction. Then think about what is included in a good summary of fiction and a good summary of nonfiction.

- The answer to a test question about summarizing will not be directly stated in the reading passage. You must think about the most important ideas to determine the best summary.

Read this article about the American sport of footbag. Then answer questions about the article. Choose the best answer for Numbers 13 and 14.

A Sport with a Kick

In 1972, two Americans invented the sport of footbag. Footbag is played with a small, round bag that is kicked and passed with the feet. Players do not touch the bag with their hands or arms. Footbag is similar to popular sports in Vietnam, Japan, China, and other Asian countries.

Footbag requires balance and flexibility. It helps develop one's coordination and concentration. Footbag kicks include the toe kick, the outside kick, the inside kick, and the knee kick. Footbag tricks mix these different kicks with moves such as stalls, spins, ducks, dives, and cross-body moves. Many footbag tricks have imaginative descriptive names like the mirage, the flying clipper, and the cloud delay.

There are several competitive footbag games. In freestyle footbag, players perform a sequence of tricks in a timed routine set to music. They are judged on the basis of artistic and technical merit. In the game of footbag net, players use their feet to kick a footbag over a five-foot net, as in volleyball or tennis. In footbag golf, players kick a footbag around hazards and into a hole.

13. What is the article mostly about?
   Ⓐ the rules of footbag golf
   Ⓑ the sport of footbag
   Ⓒ the sports played in Asian countries
   Ⓓ the types of kicks used in footbag

14. What is the best summary of the article?
   Ⓐ Footbag tricks involve kicks and moves such as stalls, spins, and ducks.
   Ⓑ Freestyle footbag, footbag net, and footbag golf are three competitive games.
   Ⓒ Footbag is an American sport in which players use only their feet to kick a small, round bag.
   Ⓓ Asian countries have sports that are similar to American footbag.

Read this story about a girl with a problem. Then answer questions about the story. Choose the best answer for Numbers 15 and 16.

Paula Bergland had always been an avid swimmer and considered herself an expert at any water activity. She had even recently become a certified lifeguard. However, when Paula's brother asked her to join him in scuba-diving classes at nearby Echo Lake, Paula declined. Paula did not want to admit that the idea of spending so much time underwater frightened her.

"Come on, Paula. You'll have fun," encouraged Brian.

"For the fifth time, no thanks," Paula firmly replied. Brian's constant nagging was beginning to frustrate his younger sister.

"How about just trying the first class?" Brian pressed. "If you don't like it, I promise I won't bother you again." Paula reluctantly agreed, believing that attending one class would be worthwhile if it quieted her brother.

The instructor began the first lesson with an introduction to scuba diving. She explained how a diver named Jacques Cousteau had invented scuba-diving equipment. She then demonstrated how the equipment was worn and used.

Paula found the first class so intriguing that she returned for the second session. Eventually, she accompanied Brian to all ten sessions. By the end of the final class, Paula realized that she had learned not only how to scuba dive, but something else as well. Paula learned that some things are not so frightening once you learn more about them.

15. What is the main problem in the story?

　Ⓐ　A girl worries that she won't enjoy a scuba-diving class.

　Ⓑ　A girl who is an avid swimmer is suddenly afraid of the water.

　Ⓒ　A girl is frightened by the idea of learning how to scuba dive.

　Ⓓ　A girl is frustrated by the constant nagging of her older brother.

16. Which of these best summarizes the story?

　Ⓐ　A boy learns that nagging can be a useful means of encouragement.

　Ⓑ　A brother and sister work together to help each other master a new skill.

　Ⓒ　A girl comes to accept that she doesn't have to be the best at everything she does.

　Ⓓ　A girl learns that trying something new may be frightening, but it can also be fun.

Read this story about a basketball game. Then answer questions about the story. Choose the best answer for Numbers 1 through 6.

Throwing in the Towel

It was the last basketball game of a long, losing season, and Rachel Lewis could take no more. She couldn't wait for the game-ending buzzer to go off and end this torturous game.

"Pass the ball! Pass it, pass it!" Rachel yelled, her voice snippety as she maneuvered under the net so she could take a shot. Tia, her teammate, did manage to pass the ball in Rachel's direction, but Rachel was too far under the net to make an easy catch. As Rachel lunged awkwardly for the ball and knocked it out of bounds, she shook her head and rolled her eyes. "Great pass," she murmured to herself.

"Rachel, get in the game," shouted her coach and older sister, Carla.

Rachel's eyes darted to her coach, then to Number 12, the player she was supposed to defend. Number 12 raced up the court, received a pass, launched the ball, and scored three points all in the blink of an eye. Rachel sighed heavily, her shoulders sagging, as she lumbered down the court. "Lucky shot," she whispered as Number 12 went back down the court.

On the next possession, Rachel got the ball and ran down the court dribbling. But as she prepared for a superstar shot, Number 12 reached and dislodged the ball from Rachel's hands. As the ball bounced down the court, Number 12 raced down the court in full pursuit, lassoed the ball, dribbled to the basket, and scored two more points.

"Time out," Carla called to the referee as she shot a concerned look at her sister. The referee blew his whistle and the two teams went to the sidelines. Rachel kicked her team jacket that rested on the floor by the team's bench.

Carla approached her younger sister quietly. "Rachel, what's going on with you? You're not playing well at all. In fact, you look as if you're ready to throw in the towel."

Rachel kicked the jacket again, her left shoe squeaking across the floor. "Well, I'm not sure, but it might have something to do with the fact that this is the last game of the year and we've only managed to win two games all season."

"Well, if you decide to adopt a losing attitude to go with the losing record, then you will never learn to win," Carla said. "And, I know a thing about losing. Remember my high school team? We didn't win a single game in two years. It feels lousy when you lose, but when you win, all those feelings about losing go away." Carla paused a moment and laughed. "You can trust me on that."

A cautious smile inched across Rachel's face. She wasn't too sure about her sister's advice, but after listening to her she did realize one thing—winning two games for the season would be better than winning none. If ending the year on a positive note helped build that optimism for next year, then Rachel would give a last ditch effort.

Identifying Author's Purpose

1. What is the author's purpose in the first paragraph?
   - Ⓐ to show why Rachel was frustrated
   - Ⓑ to persuade readers that Rachel was an excellent player
   - Ⓒ to explain why Rachel wasn't playing well
   - Ⓓ to describe Rachel's attitude

Interpreting Figurative Language

4. What does *throw in the towel* mean?
   - Ⓐ "get in the way"
   - Ⓑ "come to an end"
   - Ⓒ "become annoyed"
   - Ⓓ "give up"

Identifying Author's Purpose

2. The story was written mainly to
   - Ⓐ describe how a basketball game is played.
   - Ⓑ entertain readers with a story that teaches a lesson.
   - Ⓒ explain the role of a coach in a basketball game.
   - Ⓓ convince readers that losing doesn't matter.

Summarizing

5. What is the main problem in the story?
   - Ⓐ A girl is frustrated that her basketball team has had a losing season.
   - Ⓑ A coach is very upset that one of her players is not playing up to her ability.
   - Ⓒ A team tries to adopt a winning attitude for the final game of the season.
   - Ⓓ A basketball player makes one mistake after another on the court.

Interpreting Figurative Language

3. A *last ditch effort* is
   - Ⓐ a final attempt.
   - Ⓑ a losing attitude.
   - Ⓒ a sudden awareness.
   - Ⓓ thoughtful advice.

Summarizing

6. Which of these best summarizes the story?
   - Ⓐ A basketball team suffers one loss after another.
   - Ⓑ A coach becomes upset with a basketball player who is not playing up to her ability.
   - Ⓒ A girl decides to change her losing attitude during a frustrating basketball game.
   - Ⓓ A basketball player almost loses a game for her team because she has a losing attitude.

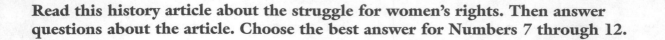

Read this history article about the struggle for women's rights. Then answer questions about the article. Choose the best answer for Numbers 7 through 12.

Elizabeth Cady Stanton

In the United States, the fight for women's rights, particularly the right to vote, was a long struggle. It began as an organized movement in 1848 in Seneca Falls, New York. The first Women's Rights Convention met there to discuss the social, civil, and religious rights of women. Elizabeth Cady Stanton was one of its organizers. She presented the Declaration of Rights and Sentiments. This document established the goals of the women's rights movement well into the twentieth century.

The Declaration of Rights and Sentiments stated that women were equal to men and deserved to be treated as such under the law. It demanded women's equality in education, commerce, industry, the professions, and public affairs. It demanded that women have equality in marriage, including the right to own property and keep their wages. Most of all, the declaration stressed women's right to vote.

When the Declaration of Rights and Sentiments was presented to the convention, not everyone agreed with it. Some didn't believe that women should have certain rights at all. The right to vote was the most controversial.

By 1860, Susan B. Anthony and other women had won some rights for married women. But this was in the state of New York, not on a national level. Married women had the right to own property, control their own money, and have charge over their children. Several other states passed similar laws. However, women still had not obtained the vote, and some women feared that obtaining this right was an eternity away.

During the Civil War, women's rights leaders focused on the abolition of slavery and the rights of African Americans. In the process, some of the legal gains that women had achieved on the state level were lost.

After the war, two amendments were proposed to the Constitution. The amendments extended rights to former slaves. In 1868, the Fourteenth Amendment recognized all persons born or naturalized in the United States as citizens. It also protected the right to vote of all male citizens. Two years later, the Fifteenth Amendment guaranteed African Americans the right to vote.

Anthony, Stanton, and their supporters refused to support the Fifteenth Amendment because it did not include women. Other women's rights leaders, including Lucy Stone and Julia Ward Howe, believed that they should bide their time. They believed that women would not gain the vote until African American men had gained it.

As a result, the women's rights movement split into two organizations with differing goals. Anthony led the National Woman Suffrage Association. This group pressed for voting rights on the federal level. Stone led the American Woman Suffrage Association. This group sought voting rights state by state. But by 1890, only a handful of states had approved the ballot for women. The two organizations merged into one movement, the National American Woman Suffrage Association.

As the nineteenth century came to a close, younger women, including Carrie Chapman Catt and Alice Paul, took the place of earlier leaders. These strong women persevered. Finally, in 1920, Congress passed the Nineteenth Amendment, granting all women the right to vote.

Identifying Author's Purpose

7. The article was written mainly to
   - (A) describe life for women during the nineteenth and twentieth centuries.
   - (B) inform readers about major events in the fight for women's rights.
   - (C) entertain readers with enjoyable stories about brave leaders.
   - (D) persuade readers to join the women's rights movement.

Identifying Author's Purpose

8. The author's purpose in paragraph 2 is to
   - (A) provide background information about women's rights in education.
   - (B) explain the content of the Declaration of Rights and Sentiments.
   - (C) convince readers that women and men are equal.
   - (D) share a personal story about Elizabeth Cady Stanton.

Interpreting Figurative Language

9. In the article, *bide their time* means
   - (A) "do without hurrying."
   - (B) "act before a certain date."
   - (C) "wait until the right moment to carry out a plan."
   - (D) "delay action until everything is planned and everyone is ready."

Interpreting Figurative Language

10. The phrase *was an eternity away* is an example of
    - (A) hyperbole.
    - (B) personification.
    - (C) a simile.
    - (D) a metaphor.

Summarizing

11. What happened next after the Fifteenth Amendment was passed?
    - (A) African Americans began to fight for the right to vote.
    - (B) Two women's rights organizations merged into one movement.
    - (C) The women's movement split into two separate groups.
    - (D) Women won the right to vote in all states.

Summarizing

12. What is the best summary of the article?
    - (A) Political movements eventually lead to conflict.
    - (B) After a long struggle, the women's movement eventually achieved voting rights for women.
    - (C) Voting rights were the most controversial issue of the women's movement.
    - (D) Everyone involved in the women's movement agreed that voting rights were important.

Read this story about an ancient Greek mathematician. Then answer questions about the story. Choose the best answer for Numbers 1 through 12.

Eureka!

More than two thousand years ago on the island of Sicily, King Hiero paid a goldsmith to make a crown of solid gold. When the gold crown was delivered, King Hiero suspected that he had been cheated by the goldsmith. The king thought that the goldsmith had taken silver, which was a less-precious metal, and mixed it with the more valuable gold. There was no way to ascertain just by looking if the crown was made of a gold-silver mixture. The king wanted to know with certainty if the crown was solid gold. To solve the problem, he called upon one of the greatest thinkers, the mathematician Archimedes.

Archimedes knew that different materials have different densities. The denser a material is, the more it weighs. Since silver is lighter than gold, Archimedes knew that a gold-silver crown would have less density than a solid-gold crown. Archimedes could weigh the crown, but that would not give him the answer he needed. He also had to know the volume of the crown, or how much space it took up. It would have been easy to figure out the volume of the crown if it were a standard shape, like a bar of gold. Then he could use a formula to find the volume. He could have weighed it beside an equal volume of solid gold and compared the weights. But the crown had an irregular shape; there was no way to figure out its volume. Or was there?

Archimedes thought long and hard about the problem, which weighed heavy on his mind. One day, as he lowered himself into the water at a bathhouse, he noticed the water rising over the sides. He felt the force of the water pushing up on him, and his body seemed lighter. These experiences were nothing new. But now, with his mind on problems of density and volume, Archimedes had a brainstorm. "Eureka!" he shouted. "I've found it!" Archimedes was so thrilled with his discovery that he leaped up out of the bath and dashed through the streets shouting "Eureka!" to surprised passers-by.

Archimedes knew what he had to do. First, he placed a lump of solid gold on a weighing balance and recorded the weight. Then he hung the lump of gold from the balance and lowered the lump into a tub of water. In water, the weight of the gold lump was one nineteenth less than its weight in air. Next, Archimedes took the same measurements with the crown. He compared its weight in air with its weight in water. If the crown was solid gold, then it would lose one nineteenth of its weight in water. But in water, the crown lost more than one nineteenth of its weight. This proved that the crown was not solid gold. King Hiero was right; the goldsmith had cheated him.

Finding Main Idea

1. The story is mostly about
   Ⓐ how Archimedes used math to solve King Hiero's problem.
   Ⓑ how Archimedes discovered the formula for volume.
   Ⓒ why gold is heavier than a silver or a silver-gold mixture.
   Ⓓ why different metals have different densities.

Recalling Facts and Details

2. Which of these is true?
   Ⓐ Silver is more valuable than gold.
   Ⓑ Volume is equal to the weight of an object.
   Ⓒ The more dense a material is, the more it weighs.
   Ⓓ Silver is the least precious of all metals.

Understanding Sequence

3. The sentences below describe the steps that Archimedes followed to determine how much gold was in the crown.
   1. He weighed the lump of gold in air and in water.
   2. He compared the weight of the crown in air and in water.
   3. He weighed the crown in air and in water.
   4. He hung a lump of gold from a weighing balance.

   Which of these tells the correct order of the sentences?
   Ⓐ 1, 4, 2, 3   Ⓒ 2, 4, 1, 3
   Ⓑ 4, 1, 3, 2   Ⓓ 4, 3, 2, 1

Recognizing Cause and Effect

4. Why did the crown lose more than one nineteenth of its weight in water?
   Ⓐ It was more dense than solid gold.
   Ⓑ It was less dense than solid gold.
   Ⓒ It was made of solid gold.
   Ⓓ It weighed more than solid gold.

Comparing and Contrasting

5. In what way were Archimedes' experiences of lowering himself into the bath and lowering the lump of gold into the tub similar?
   Ⓐ His body and the gold weighed more under water.
   Ⓑ His body and the gold appeared more dense under water.
   Ⓒ The force of gravity made him and the gold sink to the bottom.
   Ⓓ The force of the water pushed up on his body and the gold.

Making Predictions

6. Predict which of these is most likely to happen next in the story.
   Ⓐ The goldsmith makes a new crown for the king.
   Ⓑ Archimedes takes another bath for more inspiration.
   Ⓒ Archimedes informs King Hiero about the nature of the crown.
   Ⓓ King Hiero punishes the goldsmith for cheating him.

Finding Word Meaning in Context

7. In the first paragraph, the best meaning for the word *ascertain* is
   - Ⓐ "determine."
   - Ⓑ "measure."
   - Ⓒ "discover."
   - Ⓓ "value."

Identifying Author's Purpose

10. The purpose of this story is to
    - Ⓐ describe the properties of different metals.
    - Ⓑ entertain readers with a story about a great problem solver.
    - Ⓒ inform readers about scientific practices in ancient times.
    - Ⓓ convince readers that King Hiero was right about the crown.

Drawing Conclusions and Making Inferences

8. Readers of the story can conclude that density is
   - Ⓐ the same property as weight.
   - Ⓑ equal to the height of an object.
   - Ⓒ the amount of water that can fill a bathtub.
   - Ⓓ the amount of matter in a unit of volume.

Interpreting Figurative Language

11. In paragraph 3, the phrase *weighed heavy on his mind* tells you that Archimedes
    - Ⓐ forgot about a problem.
    - Ⓑ solved a problem quickly.
    - Ⓒ asked for advice about a problem.
    - Ⓓ worried about a problem.

Distinguishing Between Fact and Opinion

9. Which of these is an *opinion* in the story?
   - Ⓐ Archimedes was a mathematician and a scientist.
   - Ⓑ Archimedes proved that the goldsmith had cheated the king.
   - Ⓒ Archimedes was thrilled with his discovery.
   - Ⓓ Archimedes was one of the greatest thinkers.

Summarizing

12. What is the best summary of the first paragraph?
    - Ⓐ King Hiero accuses a goldsmith of cheating him.
    - Ⓑ King Hiero hires a goldsmith to craft a crown made of solid gold.
    - Ⓒ King Hiero seeks out Archimedes to solve a problem.
    - Ⓓ King Hiero wonders how he can obtain a better crown.

Read this letter written hundreds of years ago. Then answer questions about the letter. Choose the best answer for Numbers 13 through 24.

March, 1541

Dearest Elena,

How are you, sister? I cannot believe that more than a year has passed since I last put ink to parchment. When I wrote to you last, I had just begun my commission with the Spanish governor, Francisco Coronado. However, my assignment became more than I bargained for when Coronado abandoned his post as a governor in New Spain. He has taken many of his supporters, including me, on a journey to search for a famous landmark that will make us all rich—the mysterious city of Cibola! Some people say it is a fabled city, but Coronado is confident that it exists.

Now, I know what you are thinking, dear sister. How can a city make us rich? Well, according to Coronado and some of the locals in New Spain, Cibola is no ordinary city—it is a city of gold! According to some of the stories we have heard, Cibola may be just one of seven such cities. The gold may be worth as much as, if not more than, the gold that has already been found in the Aztec kingdoms we have overtaken.

Our search began in earnest a year ago. We left New Spain with more than 400 Spaniards and 1,000 Indians. Since then we have been wandering to the north and west, searching for this land among the deserts. While we have found no sign of gold, we have made many interesting discoveries. Last July, we charged into a city that we thought was the golden city, only to realize that it was a village chiseled into the desert hills. We found no gold, but met a variety of foreigners who live in these lands. Then, last December, we encountered the most breathtaking sight. We ventured into a land with an immense valley carved into the earth by nature, with a large river that meanders this way and that through the bottomlands. How beautiful it was!

While we continue to traverse this strange and unique land, we have found no signs of gold. Many people in the expedition are disappointed. But I, dear sister, must admit that I am satisfied simply being one of the first Spaniards to explore this new land.

I must cease my correspondence, as we are about to embark on a journey east, in search of a village where boats filled with golden eagles sail in the sky. Soon I hope to send you news of more amazing discoveries.

Your loving brother,
Manuel

Finding Main Idea

13. The letter tells mainly about
  - (A) the discovery of a famous city.
  - (B) a strange and unique land with valleys and rivers.
  - (C) a man's experiences during the past year.
  - (D) a man's longing to return home after a long journey.

Recognizing Cause and Effect

16. Coronado abandoned his post as governor so that he could
  - (A) traverse new lands.
  - (B) discover a famous landmark.
  - (C) conquer Aztec kingdoms.
  - (D) search for gold wherever he could find it.

Recalling Facts and Details

14. Coronado and his men have been searching for Cibola for
  - (A) over a month.
  - (B) several weeks.
  - (C) over a year.
  - (D) several years.

Comparing and Contrasting

17. Parchment is most like
  - (A) a thick envelope.
  - (B) a colored liquid used for writing.
  - (C) a flat sheet of fabric.
  - (D) a heavy, paperlike material.

Understanding Sequence

15. Where will the men journey next?
  - (A) to the west
  - (B) to the north
  - (C) to the east
  - (D) to the south

Making Predictions

18. Which prediction is probably the most accurate?
  - (A) Coronado will soon abandon his quest.
  - (B) Coronado will return to New Spain and become governor.
  - (C) Coronado will continue his search for the city of gold for some time.
  - (D) Coronado will discover the city of gold but keep it a secret from his men.

Finding Word Meaning in Context

19. A river that meanders

Ⓐ follows a series of twists and turns.

Ⓑ is more narrow than it is wide.

Ⓒ follows a straight course.

Ⓓ moves swiftly.

Identifying Author's Purpose

22. Manuel wrote the letter to his sister mainly to

Ⓐ explain why he has not written for more than a year.

Ⓑ describe what has been found in many of the places the writer has visited.

Ⓒ convince his sister that the city of gold exists.

Ⓓ entertain his sister with humorous stories.

Drawing Conclusions and Making Inferences

20. There is enough information in the letter to suggest that

Ⓐ Coronado enjoys the beauty of new lands he and his men have discovered.

Ⓑ Manuel has no desire to be rich.

Ⓒ Coronado cares more for gold than for the people who own it.

Ⓓ Manuel is more disappointed than the others that the city has not been found.

Interpreting Figurative Language

23. In the letter, the words *more than I bargained for* tell you that Manuel's job

Ⓐ resulted in many disappointments.

Ⓑ required that he join a dangerous expedition.

Ⓒ included more duties than he thought it would.

Ⓓ took him much farther from home than he expected.

Distinguishing Between Fact and Opinion

21. Which statement from the letter expresses an *opinion*?

Ⓐ Then, last December, we encountered the most breathtaking sight.

Ⓑ We left New Spain with more than 400 Spaniards and 1,000 Indians.

Ⓒ Many people in the expedition are disappointed.

Ⓓ Since then we have been wandering to the north and west, searching for this land among the deserts.

Summarizing

24. What is the best summary of the letter?

Ⓐ A man travels across the world hoping to find strange and unique lands.

Ⓑ A man is filled with excitement at the possibility of becoming rich.

Ⓒ A man decides to help a Spanish leader conquer Aztec kingdoms.

Ⓓ A man enjoys traveling to new lands as he continues on a quest to find gold.

Read this history article about the Great Law of Peace of the Iroquois. Then answer questions about the article. Choose the best answer for Numbers 25 through 36.

New York State has long been the home to five Iroquois nations. They are the Onondaga, the Cayuga, the Oneida, the Mohawk, and the Seneca. Centuries ago, these Indian nations constantly fought among themselves. They raided one another's villages. They burned houses and cornfields and attacked the inhabitants. Each attack led to revenge.

Then, about A.D. 1450, two peacemakers developed a plan to end warfare among the neighboring nations. The two were Hiawatha, an Onondaga orator, and Deganawidah, a Huron prophet. They proposed the formation of a permanent union, or confederation, of nations to promote peace. Hiawatha and Deganawidah traveled from nation to nation to persuade each to join the alliance. Tired of war, the five nations agreed, one by one, to accept the plan.

The Iroquois Confederacy established a set of laws. It was called the Great Law of Peace. This code of laws became the constitution of the confederacy. For several centuries, the laws that bound the league together were committed to memory. They were passed down orally from generation to generation. It took seven days for the Great Law of Peace to be recited. To aid memory, symbols representing the five founding nations were woven into belts made of wampum, or shell beads. Later, the constitution was put into writing.

The Great Council was the league's governing body. It was held at the main Onondaga village. The first Great Council met about 1570. Each nation managed its own affairs. But no nation was allowed to war against another. Instead, they would take their grievances to the council for settlement. Fifty chiefs, representing the five nations, made up the council. They met annually to discuss issues of common concern. Each nation could cast only one vote at the council fire.

Every matter that came before the council was considered on both sides of the fire. On one side of the fire sat the Mohawk and the Seneca. Together they decided whether the council should hear a matter. After the Mohawk and the Seneca came to an agreement, the Cayuga and Oneida would consider the matter until they too agreed with each other. Once both sides of the fire agreed, the matter was turned over to the Onondaga chiefs, or Firekeepers, for approval. Once approved, the matter was settled once and for all.

The Iroquois' Great Law of Peace influenced the drafting of the United States Constitution. One of the Founders, Ben Franklin, recommended in 1754 that the thirteen colonies unite. He further suggested that they incorporate many Iroquois principles to establish the new democratic government. In 1787, the Founders finally adopted some of the basic concepts from the Iroquois Constitution: both governments were based on the voluntary union of separate nations or states into one entity; each nation and state retained power over its own affairs; the larger governmental union regulated affairs common to all.

a treaty wampum

Finding Main Idea

25. Which of these is an appropriate title for the article?

Ⓐ "How Governments Are Formed"

Ⓑ "Hiawatha and Other Native Americans"

Ⓒ "The Effects of the Iroquois Confederacy"

Ⓓ "Great Councils"

Recalling Facts and Details

26. Who was Hiawatha?

Ⓐ a Huron prophet

Ⓑ an Oneida chief

Ⓒ a Mohawk warrior

Ⓓ an Onondaga orator

Understanding Sequence

27. The boxes explain some of the steps for settling a matter before the Great Council.

The Mohawk and the Seneca come to an agreement.	The Cayuga and the Oneida come to an agreement.		The matter was settled once and for all.
1	2	3	4

What belongs in box 3?

Ⓐ The council makes the final decision.

Ⓑ Each chief casts a vote.

Ⓒ The Firekeepers approve the agreement.

Ⓓ The war chiefs have their say.

Recognizing Cause and Effect

28. The Iroquois wove wampum into their belts to

Ⓐ trade with colonists.

Ⓑ seal an important agreement.

Ⓒ decorate the clothing they wore to meetings of the Great Council.

Ⓓ use as a memory aid when reciting the Great Law.

Comparing and Contrasting

29. In what way were the Iroquois Constitution and the United States Constitution alike?

Ⓐ Both were respected by their leaders.

Ⓑ Both were sacred, written documents.

Ⓒ Both required yearly meetings to discuss issues of common concern.

Ⓓ Both were based on a union of separate nations or states into one confederation or country.

Making Predictions

30. Predict what would have happened if the Iroquois had not established their confederacy.

Ⓐ The nations would have continued warring against one another.

Ⓑ The lives of Hiawatha and Deganawidah would have been in danger.

Ⓒ The Iroquois would not exist as a people today.

Ⓓ The chiefs would have been overthrown by the warriors.

Finding Word Meaning in Context

31. The word *grievances*, as used in paragraph 4, means

Ⓐ "invitations."

Ⓑ "ideas."

Ⓒ "complaints."

Ⓓ "apologies."

Identifying Author's Purpose

34. What is the author's purpose in the first paragraph?

Ⓐ to describe the people of the five Iroquois nations

Ⓑ to explain the conflicts that had existed among many Iroquois nations

Ⓒ to convince readers that native peoples were skilled negotiators

Ⓓ to tell a lighthearted story about the Iroquois

Drawing Conclusions and Making Inferences

32. From the article, readers can conclude that

Ⓐ the Iroquois had a democratic form of government.

Ⓑ once the Iroquois had the Great Law, they never fought again.

Ⓒ the Founders copied the principles of the Iroquois exactly.

Ⓓ the Founders never credited the Iroquois for their contributions.

Interpreting Figurative Language

35. The phrase *once and for all* means

Ⓐ "for each one and everyone."

Ⓑ "one time only."

Ⓒ "for the first time."

Ⓓ "finally and permanently."

Distinguishing Between Fact and Opinion

33. Which of these is a *fact* about the Great Council?

Ⓐ Each nation was represented by one chief.

Ⓑ The Great Council was comprised of seven nations.

Ⓒ Each nation had one vote at the council fire.

Ⓓ The Great Council met twice a year.

Summarizing

36. What is the best summary of the article?

Ⓐ The Iroquois Confederacy was an important agreement.

Ⓑ The Great Law of Peace formed governments around the world.

Ⓒ The Great Law of Peace was an early form of democracy.

Ⓓ The United States Constitution was based on the Iroquois Constitution.

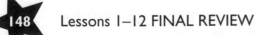

Read this retelling of an Iroquois folktale. Then answer questions about the folktale. Choose the best answer for Numbers 37 through 48.

Nekumonta and the Healing Spring

Many years ago, in a time forgotten by age, there lived a member of the Iroquois nation named Nekumonta. Nekumonta was a famed hunter throughout his land, known for his skill with a bow and arrow. Since he believed in only hunting for what he needed, he was regarded warmly by nature.

One harsh winter, as Nekumonta's tribe moved for the winter to an area near Lake Ontario, a disease ravaged their village. Several people had already died, and a fever threatened the lives of countless others, including Nekumonta's wife, Shanewis. Despairing for his people and worried about his wife, Nekumonta searched for an answer. Each night before he went to sleep, he wondered how he could help his people.

Then one night, Nekumonta had a strange dream about healing water. "I will seek out the medicine man and tell him my dream. He will know what to do."

"Your dream proves very wise," the medicine man said. "I once heard my mother's mother tell a tale about a spring of water to the north. Its properties are known to stifle the fever that grips our village."

"Then I will go in search of that spring," Nekumonta declared.

Nekumonta journeyed north from the village, carrying a small deerskin pack. He searched the forest for three days, fighting against bitter winds and deep snow. At the end of the third day, he finally stopped to rest. He gathered some withered leaves from a tree and made a soft bed to sleep on for the night.

As Nekumonta slept, the animals of the forest descended upon his sleeping place. Knowing of his respect toward nature, the animals pleaded with the great spirit named Manitou and asked him to answer Nekumonta's wishes.

Manitou sent an answer in the form of yet another dream. That night, Nekumonta dreamed of his wife turning into a majestic waterfall. "Find me and your wishes will be answered," the water sang, over and over.

Nekumonta awoke with a start near the end of the dream. Although he was still awake, he heard the singing of the waters from the earth deep below his feet. Immediately, Nekumonta began to dig into the ground. He dug slowly at first, then fast and furious. At last, a giant spring burst forth from the ground and filled the hole he had made.

Nekumonta removed a clay jar from his pack and filled it with the water. He then rushed to his village and offered the water to all who were afflicted with the fever, including his wife. In no time, they were cured of the disease.

From that day forth, Nekumonta was no longer known solely for his abilities with a bow and arrow. He was now known as the chief of healing waters, the savior of his people. From that day until this, the healing properties of springs have been used to help the sick and frail, all because of a brave hunter named Nekumonta.

Finding Main Idea

37. Which of these states the main idea of the first paragraph?

Ⓐ There was once a time in history that is now forgotten.

Ⓑ Nekumonta was a brave hunter who respected nature.

Ⓒ Nature often looks warmly upon those who respect it.

Ⓓ Long ago, hunters usually hunted with a bow and arrow.

Recalling Facts and Details

38. Who did Nekumonta go to after his first dream?

Ⓐ his wife Shanewis

Ⓑ the animals of the forest

Ⓒ the medicine man

Ⓓ the great spirit

Understanding Sequence

39. The boxes show some things that happened in the folktale.

| Nekumonta journeyed north from the village. | → | | → | Nekumonta made a soft bed of withered leaves. |

What belongs in the empty box?

Ⓐ Nekumonta woke with a start.

Ⓑ Nekumonta began to dig into the ground.

Ⓒ Nekumonta had a dream about his wife, who had turned into a waterfall.

Ⓓ Nekumonta searched for three days, fighting bitter winds and deep snow.

Recognizing Cause and Effect

40. What happened as a result of the disease?

Ⓐ Nekumonta grew weak and ill.

Ⓑ Nekumonta's wife died from a fever.

Ⓒ Nekumonta's village was wiped out.

Ⓓ Nekumonta saw many of his people die or become sick.

Comparing and Contrasting

41. What is similar about each of Nekumonta's dreams?

Ⓐ both included his wife

Ⓑ both told about healing

Ⓒ both included water

Ⓓ both gave clues about where to find a hidden spring

Making Predictions

42. What likely happened the next time the people of the village grew ill?

Ⓐ They searched for hidden springs.

Ⓑ They looked for answers in their dreams.

Ⓒ They went on a long journey to search for a cure.

Ⓓ They consulted Nekumonta for help.

Finding Word Meaning in Context

43. In the folktale, *stifle* means
- Ⓐ "bring peace to a situation or area."
- Ⓑ "use force to defeat someone or something."
- Ⓒ "put an end to something."
- Ⓓ "supply something that is needed."

Identifying Author's Purpose

46. The main purpose of the folktale is to
- Ⓐ entertain readers with a story that explains an aspect of nature.
- Ⓑ explain why springs are always used today to aid in healing.
- Ⓒ convince readers to respect nature.
- Ⓓ describe a beautiful spring.

Drawing Conclusions and Making Inferences

44. There is enough information in the folktale to conclude that
- Ⓐ no one in Nekumonta's village ever got sick again.
- Ⓑ the medicine man couldn't help the sick people because he, too, was ill.
- Ⓒ Nekumonta was unaware that the animals had pleaded on his behalf.
- Ⓓ Nekumonta did not gather enough water to help all the people who had a fever.

Interpreting Figurative Language

47. You can tell that *fast and furious* means
- Ⓐ "quickly and with lots of energy."
- Ⓑ "rapidly and with lots of anger."
- Ⓒ "suddenly and uncontrolled."
- Ⓓ "with a force greater than what is required."

Distinguishing Between Fact and Opinion

45. Which statement from the folktale expresses an *opinion*?
- Ⓐ "I will go in search of that spring."
- Ⓑ "Your dream proves very wise."
- Ⓒ "I will seek out the medicine man and tell him my dream."
- Ⓓ "I once heard my mother's mother tell a tale about a spring of water to the north."

Summarizing

48. What is the best summary of the folktale?
- Ⓐ A hunter is helped on a journey by the animals of the forest.
- Ⓑ A hunter goes on a journey that he hopes will help the people of his village.
- Ⓒ A hunter finds an underground spring after being guided by his dreams.
- Ⓓ A hunter is rewarded for his respect for nature by finding a cure to a deadly disease.